MW00623620

LIBRARY OF
PDB
PAUL D. MALTZER C. I. 1983

Tales of Grandpa and Gum Branch

An Historical Fiction Novel by
RUSSELL GROOVER

Edited by Eugene Y. Smith, Articulate, INK.

COVER ART & ILLUSTRATIONS
BY DOREYL AMMONS CAIN

AMMONS COMMUNICATIONS, LTD.
55 WOODY HAMPTON ROAD, SYLVA, NC 28779

COPYRIGHT © 1997 BY RUSSELL GROOVER
ALL RIGHTS RESERVED.

First Edition

PUBLISHED BY:

AMMONS COMMUNICATIONS, LTD.
55 WOODY HAMPTON ROAD, SYLVA, NC 28779
PHONE & FAX 1-704-631-0414

LIBRARY OF CONGRESS CATALOG CARD NO: 97-071081

ISBN: 0-9651232-2-7

In Dedication

Eugene Talmadge Groover
May 24, 1933 - December 1, 1993

Richard Russell Groover

On February 3, 1937, in the Gum Branch section of Liberty County, Georgia, Richard Russell Groover was born at home to John T. and Louise Groover. His earliest memories were of living on the farm with his grandparents, Redding and Mary Groover.

In 1947, Russell's family moved to Tampa, Florida; however, every summer until he was seventeen, Russell worked on family farms back in Gum Branch.

After graduation from Hillsborough High School in 1954, he joined the Tampa Police Department where he became a motorcycle policeman, eventually training other riders.

Upon retirement, Russell went into the motorcycle and real estate businesses. And then, after his wife, Carol, passed away, he moved to the Croom area of the Withlacooche State Forest in Florida (1992).

Because of his real estate purchases in the Sylva area of Western North Carolina, Russell spent a good deal of his time there. It was here that he began to write. His first article was published by the *American Motorcyclist* in 1995. <u>Tales</u> <u>of</u> <u>Grandpa</u> <u>and</u> <u>Gum Branch</u> is his first novel.

Russell has three children: Melody Whitaker, John Groover and Tracy Groover. His grandchildren are Zack Whitaker and Erica Ritter.

PREFACE

With each new day, as I wake I look out my window. There I see the familiar outline of pine trees reaching to the sky almost identical to the pines I once saw from the front porch of our farm in Gum Branch. The only sounds other than the distant interstate traffic hum are those of the forest. A doe and her fawn graze in the tall bahia grass along the fence. A blue jay and a cardinal give color to a bird feeder with its top set askew by the night's visit of a hungry raccoon. I smile and think, "Grandpa would have probably said ... 'I know he was a daddy coon because he left the lid up.'"

The Lord has favored me once again and set me down in my own Gum Branch similar to the one in which he placed me over sixty years ago, except this one isn't in southeast Georgia. This one is in the Croom area of the Withlacooche Forest in Florida, one tiny piece of land that He saved just for me in the middle of three thousand acres of a state-owned wildlife management park.

Gum Branch is located in Liberty County, Georgia, along Highway 196 about halfway between Hinesville and Glennville. The Gum Branch signs along the road are placed in a community that was once named Providence. There is a small hand-painted sign on a pine tree beside the highway advising travelers of that fact. The original Gum Branch is about three or four miles west of there in the area where the Gum Branch and the Liberty Baptist churches set across the road from each other next to their mutual cemetery.

I can still see the spirit of the people who settled the area almost two hundred years ago in their descendants—ambitious, honest, hard-working people who are the backbone of this country. Over the years when I have felt that our nation has lost the values that once made it great, I have returned here and seen that those values are still alive and well, and I have realized that as long as small communities like this survive, our country will also.

Grandpa was a fun-loving, hard-working man who would take time to help his neighbors and talk to a child. I was privileged to be a youngster who benefited from his love and knowledge the last few years of his life.

"Uncle Redding" is what everyone called him,

even those who were not related. He earned that name because of his caring and he wore it well. I found it was impossible to write a story about Grandpa without writing about Gum Branch. The spirit that flowed through him was the same spirit that flowed through the people that made up Gum Branch, and the two could not be separated.

Over the years I have told the tales of Grandpa's antics at cookouts and little get-togethers, to the amusement of friends and family. Lately, my granddaughter, Erica, would come up and ask me to tell the stories over and over again every time a new visitor would join our little group, fearing that they might never hear about Grandpa and Gum Branch.

One day when I was telling stories about Grandpa to a dear friend of mine, Sue Yowell of Sylva, North Carolina, she suggested that I write them down, maybe even put them in a book. She backed it up with a gift to attend a writer's seminar at Catch the Spirit of Appalachia, conducted by author Amy Garza, and her sister, Doreyl Ammons. My venture into the world of the gifted was an uneasy one to say the least. As Grandpa would have put it, "I was going bear hunting and I only had a switch." I knew my shortcomings in the world of communications, they had been pointed out to me numerous times by my teachers and almost anyone else who could write the English language.

The gathering reeked with intellect, and I felt like just sneaking out and going for a ride in the mountains until I saw a friendly face over in the corner of the room that put me at ease. I thought to myself, "I have an ally. If she can stay for the seminar, so can I." You can imagine my surprise when I found she was the author who was conducting the seminar. The day flew by and Amy reached deep down inside me and pulled out the confidence that it took for me to tackle the task I was about to undertake. So there I went, kicking and screaming into the world of literature.

The mind trip back to visit Grandpa and Gum Branch has been an emotional one. As I wrote, I found myself with tears in my eyes one minute and laughing out loud the next. Phone calls to family members like Glenn Groover whom I hadn't seen in years were rewarding themselves, and when I talked to Cousin Jack I caught a glimpse of the same humor that had been passed down my side of the family, too—or was it Gum Branch? I tried to remember some of the simple things, like curing tobacco and cooking syrup, but the actual process escaped me. A call to cousins Miles and Tracy made me realize these things should be written down too. It might not have been the way agriculture experts said it should be done, but it was the way it was done in Gum Branch and that is important. I want to thank Joann Kicklighter for her help, too. And there are Joyce and Alyson Ritter who spent hours upon hours trying to decipher my spelling and aim me down the road toward some semblance of the English language. They made the trip a lot easier.

My daughter Melody gave me the idea for an illustration when she presented me with a sketch from a photo of Grandpa and me for my birthday. My son Tracy didn't try to tell me how to write, but he let me know whether I was on the mark or not. And my oldest son, John, who was properly named after my father, made me remember the times Dad kept things hopping.

Most of all, I want to thank the people of Gum Branch for helping to raise me into the person I have become.

— *Russell Groover*

John T., Russell and Louise Groover
Winter of 1940 at the old farm

TALES OF GRANDPA AND GUM BRANCH
CONTENTS

$\mathfrak{H}$OMER

As I pulled off Highway 196 onto the little dirt road a twinge of nostalgia swept over me, mellowing the present. Slowing the truck, I leaned close to the steering wheel and searched the area. The fall air whispered through the trees, teasing the newly colored leaves as I gazed at the old Gum Branch bridge. It's timbered planks had borne the weight of military vehicles crossing the branch during World War II. A little farther on I could see the limbs of the giant oak tree sheltering part of the road where our farmhouse once stood.

The fields seemed a lot smaller now than when I was a kid. All of the pecan trees and the grapevines were gone, and only a few of the pear trees still stood. For just a split second I thought I caught a glimpse of an elderly gray-haired man among the pines behind the field. I pulled over and stopped under the oak that Grandpa had sworn was the grave of a man, and let the sentimental feeling of the old homeplace wash over me.

Cousin Talmadge had just passed away; his death had brought home to me that he was the first, and the others of us from that time were of the age of possibility. My heart full, I said aloud, "When we're gone, the memory of Grandpa and the others who lived in the original Gum Branch will be lost forever. Our children and their descendants should have some kind of insight into those who have come before ... not just names on a page."

So my need to tell the stories about Grandpa and Gum Branch began.

The best way to acquaint you with Grandpa is with a story about Homer, a young man who had come to see my daughter some years past. Although Grandpa had passed away thirty-five years before this story happened, his influence was present then and lives on now.

On that evening, our three dogs in the back yard whined restlessly. They longed to be set free for their usual evening hunt back across Seventeen Mile Run into the woods. My daughter, Melody, was in her bedroom putting on the finishing touches for this first date with Homer, who had just started working with her at the supermarket. Her two brothers, Tracy and John, and I were preparing a special welcome for Homer, sort of an initiation to see if he was worthy to date Melody.

Homer wheeled his daddy's station wagon into our driveway and came to a showoff stop, letting the front end bounce up and down a few times to demonstrate his cool driving. He sported a brand new haircut that showed a little too much ear, and his khaki pants had a crease down the front so sharp that it could have probably cut paper. His long-sleeve white shirt collar was starched so stiff his neck had already been rubbed red. Homer double-checked his slicked-back red hair in the side mirror, then looked cautiously at the three dirt bikes parked in the front yard, not knowing that the biggest and baddest one belonged to the sweet dainty girl with whom he had a date.

John manned the front door while peeking from behind the drapes to calculate Homer's progress up the front sidewalk. Tracy went to the back and let the dogs in so they could be set free out the front as usual. Tracy had a special knack for getting the dogs stirred up. He'd talk to them in a low anxious tone, saying "Where's it at?" and "Ready to go hunt?" This would start them whining and jockeying for position to see who would be the first one out the door.

Tension filled the air as Homer drew closer. Then at the right moment John threw the door open and yelled, "GET 'UM!"

Those three dogs hit the screen door so hard they nearly knocked it off the hinges.

Homer's expression was that of sheer terror when he saw those snarling, yelping, growling, killing machines bearing down on him. Without hesitation, he turned and ran for his life. Unknowingly, however, he took the same route around the house the dogs did and became tangled within the hunting pack. We watched as Homer was spat out by the group of dogs, but to our amazement, he didn't stop. He had the adrenaline flowing at full splash, making sure he was out of harm's way before sliding to a stop on the bank of the creek.

We approached Homer with caution, not sure whether the wild look in his eyes meant he had lost it or not. He had just caught his breath as I held out my hand and said, "Hello, I'm Melody's dad. You must be Homer." Not waiting for an answer, I went on, "This is Tracy and John, Melody's two brothers."

Homer, still panting, shook his head in acknowledgment. Putting my hand on Homer's shoulder, I said, "Come on in the house, son. I'll fix you a glass of ice tea and you can tell us all about yourself while Melody finishes dressing."

And that's the story of how Homer made his way into the history of our family.

Those who have heard this story think it was a horrible trick we played on Homer, but let me tell you how Homer felt about it when I ran into him and his family twenty years later at the mall.

"Mr. Groover, I'd like you to meet my wife and kids," Homer started.

Before the introductions could be completed, little carrot top, Homer Jr., asked, "Gee, dad, is this the Mister Groover that set the dogs on you?"

Homer gave a proud smile and said, "It sure is, son!"

Homer then told me the dog incident was probably the most exciting thing that had ever happened in his life; that he had become sort of a neighborhood hero. It seems that his kids would bring their little friends over and they would all sit around and listen with amazement as the story would be repeated for the umpteenth time.

I smiled and said, "Homer, you're a legend in our family, too, and all our friends that have heard the story feel they know you personally."

Homer smiled and thanked me again as he and his family parted.

With a warm feeling deep inside I thought of all the legends my Grandpa had created. Some of the people had been gone for a century and their stories were still being told. Now Homer had more or less become immortal, as his descendants and my Grandpa's will repeat his story generation after generation.

ᴚ REDDING MILES GROOVER

On a cold and wet evening in southeast Georgia my grandpa, Redding Miles Groover was born to Charles and Rebecca Groover. That day, February 19, 1860, Redding became the fifth child in a family that would grow to include ten brothers and sisters. Less than a year later his father entered the Confederate Army, and was commissioned a second lieutenant soon thereafter.

The last year of the war imprinted deeply in Redding's memory and would remain vivid until he died. He remembered the Union army raiding the farm and cleaning out the smokehouse and then loading all of the seed and cattle feed into their wagons, the soldiers taking bets as they shot the yard chickens. He also remembered three soldiers dragging his older sister off into the woods with her fighting and screaming, and he remembered her returning the next day, ashamed for anyone to look at her. He also remembered the sergeant who returned after the troops left and gave them back a ham, apologizing and saying, "This is war."

Charles came home after the war to find his family living on wild plants and game they could snare, and his fifteen-year-old daughter pregnant. And a new fear had entered their lives—the "'fore [before] day riders." This was a gang of slaves who had been freed from the British-owned plantations along coastal Georgia. Before daylight, they would raid the homes of small farmers—those who had never owned slaves—killing, raping, looting, and sometimes burning the houses and barns to the ground. Charles moved his family to a clearing in the middle of a swamp where a makeshift hut served as their shelter until the "'fore day riders" were rounded up by a band of farmers.

Rebuilding was upmost in Charles' mind as he took Redding with him from farm to farm, trying to find seed to plant a crop. When seed was found, there was no money exchanged, just a promise and a handshake.

Redding was just seven years old when his father assigned him the job of providing the family with wild game to supplement their diet. He took the job very seriously, never wasting a shot. From that time on he treated wildlife sacred and only killed to protect or to eat but never as a game.

Redding was thirteen when he and his younger brother Minzie were helping their father clear new ground for planting at what is now known as the Loyall Groover farm. Charles stopped working and sat on a log they had just trimmed. Holding his head down, he told the two boys to go to the house and bring back a jug of water while he rested. When they returned a few minutes later they found their dad lying beside the log on his back. Thinking he was taking a nap, they waited for a while before they tried to wake him. After their repeated attempts were unsuccessful they went to get their mother, who sent them to the next farm for help while she ran to look after Charles.

Charles Allen Groover was forty-four when he died, leaving behind his wife and ten children ranging in ages from one to twenty-four years old. He left them a legacy of love for their fellow man, God and family first, and the fact that you should never take your own self too seriously.

William, the oldest brother, farmed with the help of Minzie, Hamp, and Alex, while Redding went looking for a job that would bring much needed money to the family for essentials. The only job he could find at that time was shoveling sawdust at a sawmill nearby. Hard work, a habit his father had taught him, paid off, and he caught the attention of a timber buyer from the Dunn-Levi Lumber Company of Savannah. The buyer gave Redding a mule to ride in exchange for help locating certain tracts of land in Liberty and Long Counties. Watching carefully and asking the right questions, he learned a trade that he followed most of his life: a woods rider, sometimes called a timber cruiser.

Weekends were spent back in Gum Branch where the telling of tall tales was fast becoming an art. Redding would start out, "I saw one of the biggest rattlesnakes I have ever seen in my life yesterday. It was so big around I thought it was a tree that fell across the trail."

"How big wuz the rattlers?" Minzie asked.

"You'll have to speak up, Minzie," Redding said, "I can't hear a word you're saying. The rattlers sang so loud, it nearly deafened me."

"I shore wish you could have brung him home with you," Minzie said. "We could'a hooked him to the wagon to help pull that five-hundred-pound watermelon we grew."

Gum Branch Baptist Church was started in the mid 1800s on land donated by Mr. Long for the church and cemetery. The primary organizers were the Groover, Zorn, Smiley, and Long families.

Everybody always went to church on Sunday even though the preacher only came on the second and fourth Sundays. It was on one of these Sundays when Redding met his first love, Rachel Gillmore, the preacher's daughter.

Reverend Gillmore and his family always stayed the Saturday night before the fourth Sunday at the Groover farm. On one of these Saturday nights Redding and Rachel slipped out for a moonlight walk. When they got back, the Reverend and his wife were waiting for them, fit to be tied. Gum Branch Baptist Church had to find a new preacher and Redding had to ride his mule fourteen miles one way to Glenville on Sundays just to sit beside Rachel in church. Later, Reverend Gillmore moved to north Georgia and Rachel was forbidden to ever write Redding.

The Zorn family, very educated and first generation in this country from Germany, didn't exactly fit in. They gave the impression they were better than anyone else, what you might call snobs.

This attitude was a challenge to Redding. Their daughter Mary was a frail but sassy girl about his age, and every chance he got he would say something to her to get her started with her smart remarks and quick comebacks. These bouts would end with laughter from their friends, then a smoothing of Mary's feathers, so to speak.

Mary Mozell Zorn, called "Molly" by Redding, was born December 25, 1859. She was the eldest of the children and became real familiar with the "pecking order." Some say she was once a shy girl until one day at school when the sky turned dark and a thunderstorm gathered. All of a sudden, a huge ball of fire came through the door of the little one-room schoolhouse and went out an open window. The thunder was deafening and the air was filled with a smell of burning wood and cloth. Molly lay on the floor unconscious, her black dress smoldering. The teacher sent one boy on a mule to Hinesville to fetch the doctor and another to the Zorn farm for her father. It was several weeks before the burn on Molly's side was healed, and she had changed into a bitter person.

Molly grew into a beautiful young lady with smooth olive skin, but her attitude kept suitors away. She had resigned herself to being a spinster. And then Redding's persistence and easygoing manner began to attract Molly. His quick laughter at her cutting remarks eventually disarmed her and he became her one and only beau. Their courtship lasted for about a year, with all of their meetings being at church or chaperoned in the formal living room of the Zorn farm.

Redding was nervous the evening he asked her father for Molly's hand. Mr. Zorn looked at Redding with displeasure, and with the authority that only he could muster, he said, "Redding, Molly will be marrying well below her station if she marries a Groover. We come from a well bred and educated German family. You are an ignorant farm boy who doesn't have a thing, much less a future, and you won't ever be able to support her."

Redding felt a burning inside. He had not been intimidated. Fire flashed in his eyes as he rose from his chair, putting a visible fear in James Zorn's heart. "Molly will be cared for and never go hungry," Redding said through clenched teeth. "I will be back next Saturday for your answer."

Redding rode away on his mule without the usual parting courtesies to Mrs. Zorn and Molly.

Friends and family from Gum Branch and Providence gathered at the Zorn farm for the wedding, with wagons and carriages lining both sides of the roads. Long tables under the oak trees held every special dish imaginable, brought by the community wives for the reception.

Redding loaded Molly's belongings onto the wagon and they left for what Molly thought would be the Groover farm. It was the custom in those days for newlyweds to live with the groom's parents until they could afford to build their own home, usually on land given by a parent.

The mule pulling the wagon held his head high and went into a trot as they turned onto a small path off the main road.

"Where are you taking me?" Molly said with alarm.

"I got a surprise for you," he said. "I bought the old Todd place awhile back and fixed it up so you would have a home of your own to start with."

The little log cabin came into sight as they rounded the last turn in the trail and the mule quickened his pace.

"Sure is a ugly little place," Molly started. "I know that roof probably leaks. The pump looks to be about fifty foot out in the back yard—ours was right on the back porch. I imagine you got rats as big as squirrels all in the house."

The remarks cut Redding deeply. He had spent months after work making the rundown log house livable, splitting shingles by firelight, and making a two-day trip all the way to Savannah to buy glass for the windows.

Molly continued her fault-finding inspection while Redding unloaded the wagon and turned the mule loose.

She complained about the wood being too damp to cook with and about the smell rising off the new stove as she prepared their meal. For the first time Redding was not amused by the feisty young lady that he had taken as his wife.

"Where do you think you going to sleep?" Molly said sharply. "You shore ain't gonna sleep in the same bed as me."

After two weeks things had only gotten worse and the marriage had not been consummated. Redding made a decision. "Get your things together, Molly," he said.

"And where do you think you are taking me?" she responded as curtly.

"Back to your mammy," Redding answered. "I took you for a wife but you ain't one. I'll just have to find me another one somewhere else."

The trip back was slow and solemn. The only sounds were the ring of the trace chains on the harness and the soft shuffle the mule's hoofs made as they hit the south Georgia sand.

Mrs. Zorn came out on the front porch as they pulled the wagon up in front of the house.

"Well, how are the newlyweds doing?" she asked as she wiped her hands on her apron.

"Come on in, I almost got dinner ready."

"I can't stay, Mrs. Zorn," Redding said. "I got to go on. I uh ... Molly ain't gonna make a wife for anybody, so I brung her back to you."

"Molly, what in the world is wrong with you?" her mother asked.

"He actually tried to lay in the same bed as me," she answered, "and I remember what the Bible says about things like that."

Mrs. Zorn was left standing on the front porch wringing her hands as Redding drove away and Molly went inside. "What is everyone at church going to say?" she moaned.

Two weeks later, Mr. and Mrs. Zorn returned Molly and her luggage to Redding's little log cabin, where their marriage became valid.

The little place Redding had bought turned out to be poor farmland. Two dry crop years just about wiped him out. The little bit of money he made working at the sawmill and cruising timber locally went to food and clothes for his and Molly's growing family. Cash money was so hard to come by that he missed two mortgage payments.

The banks in those days had a lot more power than they do now. At any time they could call in your loan for payment in full, and if you couldn't get another loan in thirty days to pay them off, you were thrown out and the bank owned the land. This was a common practice after the Civil War because most banks were owned by Northerners and they were grabbing all the farm-

land they could get their hands on. After the fore-
closure the "kindhearted" banker would allow the
previous owner to stay on as a sharecropper until
his farm could be sold for a huge profit.

Redding wasn't going to farm his own land for
someone else—land on which he had made payments for ten years. He had heard about seventy-
two acres with a shanty on it that was coming up
for sale. Redding knew about the place from hunting and cruising timber. Only about ten acres had
been cleared for farming—the rest was swamp
and pine timber. He figured there would be no way
to make a living farming, especially if it rained
very much, but there was enough turpentine timber that he might make a go of it with help from
his growing family and his brothers.

The previous owner had passed away and the
family had moved to Savannah. With a lot of hag-
gling, a deal was made. The down payment would
be five dollars in cash, a brood sow, and his prized
rifle—and five dollars a month for twelve months.

Molly wasn't a bit happy about leaving the little house she had complained so much about and
moving into the shanty. She let it be well known.
But before long, Redding, with the help of his
brothers, cut logs and expanded the front porch,
and soon the shanty blossomed into a pretty
decent looking log cabin.

FLOATING LOGS

Cruising timber took Grandpa all over south Georgia and most of Florida. At slack times he and his brothers would hire on with another lumber company out of Lumber City, Georgia. Their job would be to float logs down the Altamaha River to the huge sawmills in Brunswick.

The logs were tied together in rafts, and as the current took them downriver, they would use long poles to steer with and help keep them in some kind of navigable order. All along the river were old deserted fishing shanties available for shelter at night or during stormy weather. On one of these nightly layovers they started telling stories about the previous log floats they had made and their trouble with snakes and alligators. Well, as usual, the tales got a little out of hand and the first-timers were getting really scared.

17

Some of them even started seeing snakes. Grandpa gathered up enough driftwood to keep the fire going all night, then announced that he was going inside and try to get a little sleep. One by one, the others followed, carrying enough straw or moss to bed down.

After a few hours of sleep Grandpa woke up and walked outside to look at the moon. One of the new men came out and asked him if there was any problem with the logs.

Not to miss such a great opportunity Grandpa said, "No, but a dadblame moccasin crawled up beside me in the straw and I ain't going to sleep in there. I bet that whole place is full of them."

"You saw a snake where?" the rookie shouted, looking behind him.

The shout brought the other sleepy loggers outside to see what the commotion was and Grandpa related the story to them. Everyone made torches and went back inside to run the snakes out, but nothing was found. His brothers looked for a sign from him like a wink or something to let them know that he was playing a prank, but he looked dead serious and revealed nothing.

Later, everyone finally went back inside and tried to sleep. About three o'clock in the morning, Minzie woke to find Grandpa clinging to an overhead rafter and looking down. "What in the world are ya'll doin' up there?" Minzie asked.

"Can't you see them?"" Grandpa said as he

changed his grip on a rafter. "They're all over the floor."

"What?"

"Snakes," he said. "There's one coming up behind you right over there."

"Where?"

By this time the other loggers were up on their feet, looking around for snakes.

"Ya'll better get up here out of the way or you're gonna get snakebit!" Grandpa warned.

A scramble for the rafters started, with the half-awake men trying to pull themselves up. Minzie slipped and fell down to the floor below, knocking his breath out. Grandpa jumped down and pretended to pick a snake up and throw it out the door, hollering "Oh, my God, it's as big around as your arm!"

Two other men reached down and helped Minzie back up into the rafters as Grandpa retreated back inside and climbed to safety. From their perch above, it appeared that the floor was alive with snakes as the moon cast shadows of moving branches through the open windows.

By the first light of day the men clinging to the rafters saw Grandpa sleeping soundly on the floor curled up on a big straw bed.

"What in the world are ya'll doin' up there?" he asked sleepily.

"Getting away from the snakes," Hamp said.

"They ain't no snakes around here," Grandpa answered. "Ya'll must've had a nightmare or something."

That day seemed especially long to all the men, and when camp was made that night they told Grandpa he had to sleep outside.

Minzie wondered as he drifted off to sleep if his brother would find more snakes out-of-doors.

ℌAPPY BIRTHDAY

The Sunday of his seventy-second birthday, Grandpa headed off to church by himself that morning as usual. Grandma had ceased going several years ago because she thought it was too much trouble; besides, she had to take a bath first, and that was not one of her favorite things to do.

After dinner, Grandma gathered her little group around her on the front porch. Ethel, the youngest daughter, sat near her. A small, frail girl, she was married to Lee, one of the best woodsmen in three counties—he also made the best moonshine. Unfortunately, Lee was his own best customer. Grandma's other two girls, Emma and Ila, also sat close by.

Emma, the middle daughter, had married

21

William ("Sweet William"), about the most worthless man to be found anywhere. He always wore a long-sleeved white shirt and begged off work because he was blind, but he could spot a squirrel in a pine tree two hundred yards away.

Ila, the oldest daughter, was the most beautiful person in the whole community—if not in appearance, in her soul. Because of her good nature and her need to please, she ended up as the family servant, not unlike Cinderella. The only difference: her prince never showed up. When she passed away while living all by herself in her late seventies, she had never been more than twenty miles from her birthplace.

Grandpa sat in the swing by himself on the other end of the porch.

"Redd'n," Grandma said in a scolding tone, "you shore made a mess at dinner when you spilled yore ice tea. Poor Ila has too much to do already without havin' to clean up behind you. If'n yore too old to hold yore glass, you aught to quit drinking at the table."

Feeling that Grandpa had been properly scorned, the little group turned their attention to gossip, searching for another victim on which to lower their wrath.

"I think I'll mosey over to Minzie's," Grandpa said, getting up from the swing.

The little group stopped their gossiping just long enough to give him a disapproving look as he left. Lee watched as the old man started across the back field towards a well-worn woods path and thought to himself, "It's three miles through the woods to Uncle Minzie's. It'll be dark way before he gets back. Nobody travels in the woods at night if they can help it. I'd better follow him an' see where he's a'goin'."

Lee tracked Grandpa at a distance. They crossed the first swamp on foot logs that had been laid to form a bridge. Lee saw a new trail just a few feet out of the swamp that he hadn't noticed before, branching to the left. The newly crushed grass told him that his prey had taken this route. Lee could only think of one farm in that direction and he cut across the underbrush so he would get there before Grandpa.

Grandpa came out of the woods at a field behind the Jenkins' farm house, stopped, looked around. When he was sure of no detection he gave a call, "Whooop, whooop, whoopeeee."

Shortly, Mrs. Jenkins came out the back door, stopped for a few minutes in the yard to look at the chickens, then disappeared into the barn.

Lee couldn't believe what he was seeing as Grandpa made his way to the barn, crouching low like a hunter stalking a deer. The Jenkins were one of the most respected families in Gum Branch. Mr. Jenkins was a deacon in the church and she taught Sunday school. Lee had even heard that her daddy was once some great preacher up around Atlanta. To get a better vantage point Lee made his way to the back of the

barn. Looking through a crack caused by a loose
board, he saw what was going on inside. He heard
rustling in the loft as hay sifted through the
cracks and drifted to the floor. A hen "kawked" as
she was displaced from her nest. The mule below
raised her head and shifted her ears forward to
better identify the sound. Two cows stopped chewing their cud for a second to watch the hay fall to
the floor. Lee thought, "Happy birthday, Uncle
Redding," then sneaked back to his hiding place
in the woods.

A little time passed, and Mrs. Jenkins
emerged from the barn, her hair tosselled, carrying chicken feed in her apron. She paused, feeding the chickens. From the woods she heard a low
call, "Whoop, whoop." With a faint smile on her
face she shook out her apron and disappeared
into the house.

Redding was startled when Lee stepped out
onto the path in front of him. "What you doing out
here, Lee?" he asked.

"Just out tracking a little, seein' if'n there's
any deer around," Lee answered. Both men began
looking at the ground, pretending to hunt for deer
tracks.

Lee broke the silence. "How long you been seeing Mrs. Jenkins, Uncle Redding?"

Grandpa was quiet for a while, then he said.
"Lee, I don't think it's gentlemanly to talk about
things like that."

Lee looked at Redding and said. "Well, I reckon

Miss Molly would like to hear about this."

Grandpa stopped and looked away. "Lee, they's a lot more to it than it shows." With reluctance Grandpa began his story as they followed the trail home while the evening shadows grew long.

"Rachel's dad was a circuit preacher a long time ago when I was just a young man. Reverend Gillmore would bring his family with him when he came to preach and they used to stay at our house sometime. I think they lived over somewhere around Vidalia. Anyway, Rachel was about fifteen years old the first time I seen her and just as pretty as a picture. Well, me and she just hit it off to start with, but her daddy didn't want her hanging around no poor farmboy, so he left Gum Branch Church and started preaching at Glennville. Ever chance I got I'd ride over there and sit by her during services. Then he moved them up to north Georgia around Atlanta. I wrote to her for a while, then one day I got a letter from her saying she caught the devil every time I wrote and her daddy would tear up the letters when he found them. Well, I kinda just quit writing, but I don't think a day ever passed that I didn't think about her." Grandpa was quiet for a while and had a faraway look in his eyes as they sat on a log and rested.

Lee mulled over what he had just heard, wondering if this was one of Uncle Redding's tall tales. "Uncle Redding," he asked, "if'n they left here when she was a young girl, how did she get back here ... in that house yonder ... married to Ralph Jenkins?"

Grandpa stood up, looked to see how far the sun had to go down, and started telling the rest of the story as they crossed the foot logs over the swamp.

"About a year after they left here, Preacher Gillmore moved them over somewhere around Rome, Georgia, where Rachel met and married Ralph, whose daddy owned a sawmill. Rachel and Ralph had three boys that grew up in the logging business. The oldest boy got married and moved out west, to Texas, I think. The other two boys were working at the sawmill one day when a wedge got knocked loose and a whole pile of logs came rolling down an' killed both of them. It wore on Rachel real bad when ever' day she could look out her window and see where her two sons got killed. Rachel had good memories of Gum Branch so she talked Ralph into moving back here about twenty-five years ago and buying the Wilkerson place where they live at now."

Lee thought for a while, then asked, "You been seeing her ever since?"

"Yep."

The two men had crossed the swamp and could see the field behind their home in the twilight. Grandpa stopped at the weathered rail fence and pulled a worn, folded envelope from his pocket. His wrinkled hand trembled slightly as he carefully opened it. Inside was a lace handkerchief yellowed with age, on one corner of which the initial "R" was embroidered. Lee took the delicate prize in his hand and looked at it, feeling the emotion it carried, then carefully handed it back to Grandpa.

Misty-eyed, Grandpa folded the handkerchief back into the envelope, performing a ceremony that he had repeated many times before. His secret treasure had been stored for another time.

Lee stayed behind, watching the elderly man cross the field, his head erect as always and his white hair blowing in the winter wind. In his mind Lee pondered over the story he had just heard. A feeling of closeness and understanding came over him for his father-in-law and he vowed to keep his secret.

28

SPOOK UNDER THE BED

Saturday nights usually meant somebody was going to spend the night at our house. More than apt it would be Uncle Clanton or Uncle Minzie, sometimes both. The purpose of these visits was to catch up on all the war news that each had heard that week and, of course, discuss the Bible, whether it be if David really deserved God's love because he was such a womanizer, or did Peter have as much faith as alleged.

One Saturday night after supper, Daddy, Grandpa, Uncle Clanton, and Uncle Minzie gathered around the fireplace in the living room with cups of coffee and started with the progress of the war.

Daddy said Patton was headed to Africa to save the British from Rommel.

Uncle Clanton said the British needed to be saved from their own selves.

And that was about all it took to get the fireworks started. Grandpa would try to get his two cents in but always stuttered with the first word, "Ander-uh ander-uh uh uh." Uncle Minzie had two stutters. One was "An-an an-an." The other was "I-I I-I." This went along with eye-blinking and grimacing. I felt real bad about them having to do this, but then one night I realized these old-timers were using this to interrupt the conversation so they could get their say.

Uncle Minzie would say, "An-an-an, I-I-uh-uh," grimace, and blink his eyes. Everybody else would stop talking to see what was going on. During their pause he would take over the conversation and have his say. I don't think the others ever caught on. I watched Grandpa do the same thing with his "Ander-uh Ander-uh."

As the night wore on the conversation would take one turn and then the other. World War II would melt back into the Bible, with plenty of evidence that we were getting close to the end of time, with Adolph Hitler surely being the Antichrist.

One by one, I watched each of them excuse himself and say he had to step out back for a minute. When they returned, they would jump right back into the fray with new vim and vigor. Finally one night my curiosity got the best of me. I couldn't believe just going to the restroom could give you that much extra vitality.

I sneaked out to the back yard and waited for the next break in the talk. Daddy came to the back of the old log kitchen, stopped by the window, looked around, then reached inside and pulled out a gallon jug. With the expertise of a professional jug drinker he flipped the jug over his right forearm and took a long swig—about two air bubbles worth—and swung the jug back down. Then he let out a loud wheeze, shook his head, coughed, and went back with new ammunition to join the battle. I stayed outside until I had seen all four come out and reload. The mystery was over.

The night wore on and one kerosene lamp ran out of fuel, leaving only one and the light from the fireplace. Uncle Minzie started nodding off, so Grandpa took him back to what was called the big bedroom where the boarders slept during the week.

Grandpa continued on with the conversation for about another half hour, then looked over at me and said, "You 'bout ready to go to bed, Dick Russell?"

"No, sir, I think I can hold out a little while longer," I said. They all had given up trying to put me to bed at a normal hour a long time ago when they found out if anybody was awake, so was I. I was afraid I might miss something.

Grandpa got up and took the remaining lamp and bid all a good night. Before leaving, he told Uncle Clanton that he could sleep in the little bedroom adjoining the living room.

Daddy and Uncle Clanton drifted around the world in their conversation to the Philippines, New Guinea, and what Doolittle had done to Tokyo. They felt that Marshall was a better general, but that MacArthur would probably be credited with winning the war in the South Pacific. The fire in the fireplace came back to life, sending a shower of sparks up the chimney as Dad poked the smoldering log. I thought to myself, "I'm glad it has started raining so we don't have to worry about setting the roof on fire again"

Uncle Clanton stood up and stretched and reckoned he would turn in, too. It had been about a half hour since Grandpa left for bed, but what nobody knew was that he had sneaked through the hall door into the little bedroom undetected and crawled under Uncle Clanton's bed, laying in wait to spring a trap.

Daddy stepped out back to get another log for the fire and a nightcap from the jug while I fixed my pallet on the floor close to the fire. Daddy came back in, threw the log on the fire and rolled another cigarette, lighting it from a twig in the

fireplace. I looked through the doorway that was left open for warmth and there I saw Grandpa laying under Uncle Clanton's bed. He smiled and put his finger to his lips, warning me not to give him away. A few minutes passed and Uncle Clanton's breathing grew deeper. With Uncle Clanton somewhere between awake and sound asleep, Grandpa pushed the bed up and let it fall.

Uncle Clanton called out, "Johnny, come in here. Something's wrong with this bed."

Daddy went to see if he was having a nightmare while I tried to muffle a laugh. Grandpa wrinkled his brow at me from under the bed, warning me to straighten up, that the prank wasn't over yet.

Daddy asked Uncle Clanton what the problem was and he told him that the bed moved. With that Daddy got down on his knees and looked under the bed. This was decision time for Grandpa—should he reach out and grab Dad and make it a two-for-one prank, or entice Daddy into joining our forces? With a frown and a shake from Grandpa's head, Dad became a player.

"Uh, Clanton, you musta been dreaming. I don't see nothing wrong with your bed," Daddy said with a serious tone in his voice.

Being satisfied with the inspection, Uncle Clanton turned over and in a short time was back to rhythmic breathing again. Grandpa pushed up with all his might and let the springs fall back on the bedstead with a bang.

Uncle Clanton came out of the bed at a dead run in his longhandles, "Johnny! Johnny! There's a spook under that bed!"

One good thing about our family, we are as good as victims as we are as participants in the jokes. Uncle Clanton laughed just as hard as anyone else when the truth became known.

Over the years I have wondered if I live to be over eighty years old like Grandpa, will I still have enough humor left in my soul to pull a stunt like that. I heard that Uncle Clanton never went to sleep at our house again without looking under the bed, especially after Grandpa passed away.

$\mathcal{H}$AINTS AND GHOSTS

I don't know if the legend about the haunted oak tree came with the farm where I was born or not, but after more than a hundred years the legend still goes on.

It seems like the previous owner loved the place so much that when he died he wanted to be buried under a certain oak tree close to the road and become part of the land and the tree forever. The legend also said that this man had been a practical joker and since this was the main road between Glennville and Hinesville, he wanted to be a ghost so he could scare the horses and travelers passing by. The legend grew and sure enough horses would get spooked when they passed under the outstretched limbs of the huge oak, especially in the twilight hours and especially if Grandpa happened to be at home.

I don't know if he told anybody else, but he told me about his special deviltry. When it was about dark and he heard a wagon or a rider coming, he would hide behind the trunk of the oak tree. At just the right moment he would wave a white cloth in the air for a second, then hide. If you know anything about horses and mules, you know that's all it takes to spook one, especially in the fading light of day.

Grandpa told each child of the family the story of the ghost. He would take them to the supposed grave under the tree and talk to the ghost, introducing them so the ghost would know that they belonged there; the ghost was to not bother them. From personal experience I can tell you that when you walked away from that tree you had the feeling of belonging to an exclusive club. My own dad was so intrigued with the story when he was young that he decided to dig under the tree and find the remains of the old man.

Grandpa convinced him that the body was actually buried in another location, and before Dad caught on to what was happening, Grandpa had a nice spot for a garden all prepared by him.

As I grew up Grandpa would include me in on the little things that keep farm life from being boring. There were still plenty of horses and wagons used for transportation in my early years. Grandpa would walk out to the road to greet the passersby and exchange news of what was happening in the community. I watched very closely as he would get the wagon driver engaged in conversation, then without being detected he would reach down and pull a hair out of the horse's flanks, which, of course, would cause the horse to kick.

"Ander-uh, I reckon yore horse must've seen that ghost," Grandpa would say, then he would turn and wink at me.

One day while we were sitting in the swing waiting for a victim to come by, I asked him how we were going to scare the cars when all the horses and wagons were gone. In his usual undefeatable manner he said, "We'll find a way." I truly believe if he had lived long enough he would have found a way.

That oak tree still stands today on the farm that is owned by his great-granddaughter, Ollis Hodges. I wonder if she is keeping the spirit happy.

One of the greatest thrills was to be scared by Grandpa. We couldn't wait until he pretended to be asleep. There was definitely a difference between the soft rumble he had when he was really sleeping and the ear-rattling snoring he let out when he faked it.

We would sneak up and touch his shoulder and wait to be scared stiff. His most common response at night would be to continue snoring and slowly turn his head toward you with his eyes rolled back where only the whites showed. Then when he was facing you fully, he would stick out his false teeth and grab your arms so there wasn't a chance of escape. Probably the one that never failed and the most subtle was when he would just sit there with his eyes closed and wait for you to touch his face, then all of a sudden he would act like a dog, snapping at your fingers and growling. I have seen kids actually lose control of body functions. We would all stand around real close in a circle on these special occasions, hoping to be the one he would choose to scare first. He would be sure that everyone was equally spooked.

If you weren't chosen until last, you would start to get that sinking feeling that maybe he didn't care any more but then when you least expected it, he would turn and give you the scare that you knew was special and better than the one he gave anyone else. I feel real sorry for those who missed this kind of great love.

To be really effective, ghost stories have to be told at special times, like on rainy or windy nights. I believe some of the ghost stories that came out of Gum Branch could have made Stephen King proud. There were several versions of the lost baby that everyone could hear but couldn't find. On windy nights the baby would get cold and start to cry ... the wind would carry the sound.

If the storyteller was really good (like Grandpa), he would start a search for the baby through dark parts of the house, and sometime he would get everybody into a situation so he could pull off a group scare. Even though you knew what was going on, you felt the thrill of the game.

We had our own headless horseman who scared many a night traveler without actually being seen. The story behind our horseman was special to the area. Back in the woods where Gum Branch Ford runs toward what is now the Fort Stewart boundary, there used to be a little farm tended by a widow, her fourteen-year-old daughter, Colleen, and twelve-year-old son, Billy.

It seems that back when the Yankee soldiers were going through the community raiding the farms, a young lieutenant saw Colleen and became aroused by her natural beauty. That evening, just about dark, he returned to the farm with the intent of kidnapping her. He rode up to the barn where she was feeding the chickens and swooped her up with one arm and tried to ride off with her. Her mother, returning from cutting oats in their field for cow feed, swung the sickle she was carrying at the rider and cut his head off.

Colleen fell to the ground unharmed and the horse continued on into the swamp with the headless lieutenant still sitting in the saddle. Billy scooped up the human head in a basket and they buried it out behind the barn, hoping to hide any evidence of the officer returning to the farm.

After the war, the family moved away, giving the farm to a relative. He tried to farm the land for a couple of years but nothing would grow in the soil. He told Grandpa that on stormy nights he would see the headless lieutenant galloping through the fields with his saber held high, trying to find his head. And when the wind blows after dark during the winter he can be heard calling, "Collleeennnn ... Collleeennn ...."

Grandpa took me across the swamp one time and showed me the little barren piece of land with only dead trees. I will never forget it.

Another ghost story that Grandpa told was about a man who worked for the railroad built close to our farm just for the purpose of hauling logs out of the swamp—he called it a tram road.

Anyway, this man was a real bully, always picking on somebody and shoving them around. A young boy about nineteen had become his latest target and couldn't seem to stay out of his way. One day when they were going back through the swamp for another load of logs, the bully tried to push the boy off the flat car. The boy side-stepped and the bully fell off the train into the swamp in a spot known to have quicksand.

The young man had the engineer stop the train while he ran back to help the bully. When he got to the spot where the bully had fallen, all he found was bubbles coming up out of the quick-sand. All of a sudden, a hand reached up out of the swamp and grabbed the boy by the ankle and dragged him right down under the quicksand.

They searched and searched but they never

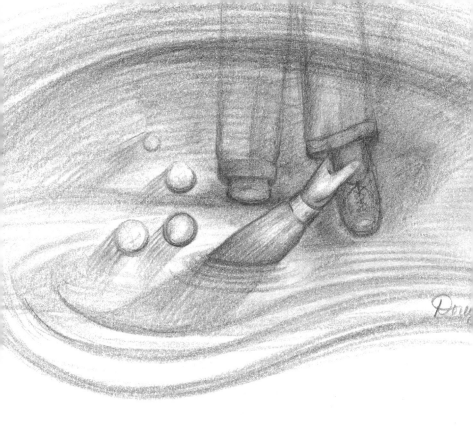

found their bodies. Grandpa would always take a break here and let the yarn sink in, then he would begin, "About two years later that young man's brother came up to our place and wanted to know if I could take him down in that swamp over there and show him where his brother drowned. I told him I would, but I had heard strange goings-on down there ... like men fighting in the night and that we shore had to be careful. Anyhow, I took this young feller right to the spot where his brother was last seen, and while we were standing there two hands come up outta the mud. One grabbed me by the ankle and the other grabbed him. I twisted and turned and got myself free. When I looked back, I saw that boy's head going down under the mud, and I heard, 'HELLO BROTHER!'"

Then Grandpa would finish up the story with, "I don't want any of you young'uns wandering around in that swamp without me 'cause I'm the only one that ever got away."

(Ollis, this is right behind your house, so be careful. I know for sure that Grandpa passed his stories down through his offspring and I hope that some of the others who were privy to his special talent picked something up, too.)

Cousin Tracy was a master at scaring kids too. I remember one time we were over at the new ground field, picking tomatoes. All of a sudden he staggered, grabbed his heart and fell on the ground and lay still. I went over and shook him a few times, knowing what was probably coming next, but he didn't respond. I had just about decided that he might not be faking when he got up with his eyes rolled back and started chasing me around, giving the best mummy impression he could muster. I knew he was faking, but I can guarantee you I was duly scared.

Miles and Talmadge always found a situation to scare Connie and me. It usually occurred about dusk when we would be walking back home from over around Robert Wells' house. They would start looking back every once in a while, then ask each other if they thought we were being followed.

I don't know if you have ever walked a dirt road in the dark of night with big shadows cast by trees moving around in the breeze or not, but trust me, it's scary. They would start walking faster and faster until we were in a full run. Needless to say, they were five or six years older than us and a lot faster. While we were trying to catch up and still looking back, they would find a place to hide, then jump out and scare us as we ran by.

On one of these night trips we were looking back and actually saw a small white object following us in the distance. We would walk faster and it would draw nearer. We would stop and it would stop and just stand there. About that time, a screech owl in a tree nearby let out his blood-curdling call, and that's all it took. Every man for himself! Miles and Talmadge didn't have to wait for Connie and me this time—we were leading the pack. Later, we found that an albino raccoon had been seen in the area. I tend to believe it was a real ghost following us.

It is sad to see those who grow past the age of a good scare. I hope I never do.

Honeybees

Honeybees and their products are very important to farm production and farm life. The bees help in the pollination of crops and in so doing they produce and make honey, a golden mouth-watering delight that goes so well with homemade biscuits.

The beeswax that stores their honey is made into all kind of products. A lot of them, like car wax, are usually taken for granted. I know this sounds a little farfetched, but the car wax that gives the best protection is based on beeswax. That goes for almost all the other paste waxes, too—from boat and furniture, to floor wax. Beeswax was used to seal in the flavor and prevent spoiling in the older canning processes. Wax seals were attached to legal documents to prove their authenticity. Wax was added to paper to keep sandwiches fresh for the schoolkids. On the farm it was used as a lubricant for hinges and things that moved, and the housewife applied wax to hand irons so they would glide smoother over starched clothes, helping to hold down rebellious shirt collars. The real biggy and the most common use was for candles, sometimes the main source of light in a home. Although candles were made from other products, too, beeswax was the easiest to use and most popular.

Farmers usually had one or two beehives around just for farm use if they didn't have bee trees in the area. We had bee trees.

One spring, Grandpa thought it was time I learned to rob a bee tree. He awoke me one morning and helped me feed the animals so we could get an early start. After breakfast we walked across the field, headed for the woods out in front of our house. Grandpa carried a flour sack over his shoulder. He helped me over the rail fence and I held the sack while he climbed over.

Grandpa talked almost the entire time we were walking through the woods. I paid close attention because he never let it be boring. He would tell me not to step on the clumps of grass because sometimes leprechauns (little people wearing green outfits) lived under there; he said they were there to help people who were lost or sad. Even though you couldn't often see them, anyone could stop and tell them their troubles, and the little people would make things right if they could.

Then there was always the old witch who had just ducked behind a tree that he saw and I barely missed. He would describe just what she looked like and what she was wearing. Somehow it always came out looking like Grandma.

"See that root over there," he would say, "you dig that up and cook it just like you cook sweet potatoes and you can live off it if you have to. Those spider webs over there—take them and put them on a fresh cut and it'll stop the bleeding. The bark on that tree—strip off a section starting at the bottom and you can make tea out of it, or if you are getting tired, chew a little piece of it and you'll feel better." The commentary would go on continuously. It was never boring.

"There he is," Grandpa said, pointing to a tiny bee just leaving a blossom. "There's our little traitor. Let's follow him and we'll find his hive."

"How do you know it's a 'he'?" I asked.

"Because little boy bees always wear pants with suspenders and yellow-and-black-striped shirts, and little girl bees wear gingham dresses and a bonnet, with their hair done up in a bun in back," he said.

"Oh," I said, straining hard to get a closer look at the bee.

We followed the bee as he went about his job of collecting—one flower to another. Grandpa stopped and stood real still for a second, signaling me to do the same. "Hear that hum?" he asked.

I listened and was able to separate the other

sounds of the forest from what Grandpa described. I nodded my head.

"Now we know where our bee tree is, we don't have to follow our little traitor anymore, and they will never know who gave their location away," Grandpa said.

It was time for another lesson. "Look around," he said. "Do you see anything that might tell you there is a bee tree somewhere close by?"

I took my time and looked at the top of the trees first. I knew it was real important that I come up with a good answer to please Grandpa. "There's an old rotten tree over there," I said. "There's probably a hive in it if it's hollow."

Grandpa gave a broad grin. "That's my boy. I'm gonna make a woods rider out of you yet."

My day had been made.

We carefully worked our way through the underbrush toward the dead tree. Grandpa stopped and motioned me forward and pointed to a clearing. There was our beehive in the tree. Grandpa led me away until we found a resting place.

"Are we going to rob the bee tree?" I asked.

"Bees are smarter than people," Grandpa said. "They work in the cool. When it gets warm, they stop and take a nap, so we'll have time to get something to eat and wait for a while."

"Looks like a good place to have dinner," he continued as he surveyed a clearing. "Do you think the deer will mind if we use their dining room?"

"I don't think so."

Grandpa took down the sack that he had been carrying over his shoulder and emptied it onto the grass. A syrup bucket, a wine bottle and an old long-sleeve shirt fell out. The wine bottle had drinking water and the bucket had two baked sweet potatoes and four biscuits in it—my favorite lunch.

"What's the shirt for, Grandpa?" I asked.

"I'll show you later," he said. Then he started telling tales about going to Savannah by wagon and the experiences he had crossing the Ogeechee Swamp. As he went on, my full stomach and the warm sun lulled me off to sleep.

"Wake up, it's time to rob the bee tree," he said.

I arose and followed him through the under-brush. I didn't hear the humming anymore. Grandpa quietly approached the bee tree, looking around to make sure there weren't any stragglers outside. He built a small fire on the ground in front of their entrance. Then he took the shirt out of the sack and tied the sleeves around the tree just above the hole. Next, he propped the tail of the shirt up over the fire with two sticks, like a tent. Then he put a handful of damp grass over the fire to make smoke. He turned, took my hand and led me to a safe place to see the action.

We watched as the smoke drifted into the opening of the tree. Inside, the bees started to stir. The hum became louder. Grandpa pointed to the top of the dead tree and we watched as the smoke chased the bees through an opening.

Just as soon as Grandpa figured it was safe, he went over and put out the fire, took the shirt down, and reached his hand up in the hollow of the tree. He pulled out a big comb of honey and dropped it into our dinner bucket.

"Come on," he said in the low tone of a thief. "Let's get outta here."

The walk home and the warm sun brought the usual questions from me. "Grandpa, why do bees make honey?"

"To feed the queen and all the baby bees."

"Won't they starve if we steal their honey?"

"No, son," he answered. "The good Lord has the bees make extra honey so they can share it with us and still have plenty left for themselves."

With the guilt removed from my mind, I held his hand as we crossed the last field, heading home.

NEW DOG

Grandpa always had a bad problem with gas. I know it isn't polite to talk about such things, but it's a fact of life. It happens to everybody, some more than others. Grandpa was at the head of the "more" classification. We would be sitting on the front porch in the swing and, sure enough, Grandpa would make himself feel better, then out of habit of saving face, he would reach over and give our old hound dog a fake kick and scold him, "Get out of here with your stink."

The poor old dog got so used to being punished for Grandpa's farts that every time he saw Grandpa start to squirm around a little, he would get that worried look on his face and start whining. When he died, we never knew if it was from old age or asphyxiation. About two days after the funeral here came another dog down the road and more or less advised us he had come to apply for the recent vacancy.

I thought this was an unusual circumstance, so I asked Grandpa how the dog knew we were fresh out of a security guard.

"Well," Grandpa said, "I heard that them dogs have a newspaper all their own and ever' day them that don't have a job read the funeral section, then try to be the first one there to take the place of the deceased. Now mind you I don't know this to be fact, it's just what I heard."

After thinking this revelation over for a few minutes it started sounding reasonable, so I accepted this explanation. I also knew if I questioned it, Grandpa would give me another scenario even more outlandish.

"New Dog," as he came to be known, had a kinda sneaky look about him and Grandpa told me to keep an eye on him, because he didn't think he could be trusted. Sure enough, about two days later we found a dead chicken in the back yard. When we questioned New Dog he flatly denied having anything to do with it, but did say that he had seen a chicken hawk flying around earlier and would bet even money that that hawk was the culprit.

Next came the eggs. We started finding empty eggshells around everywhere. There is one thing Grandpa declared he couldn't stand and that was a lying, suck-egg dog. I knew right away that New Dog's days on our farm were numbered.

Grandpa first tried just chasing him down to the end of the lane, cussing him in dog language, "Getaoutahereyouthundabit." This didn't work, and Grandpa came walking back, out of breath, with the dog following behind at a safe distance.

Next was the "we are going for a ride" ploy. He put New Dog up in the back seat of his old Model A and away they went, headed toward Gum Branch Ford, the dog sitting upright and proper just like you are supposed to look when you are being chauffeured. Thirty minutes later here comes Grandpa, driving his old Model A back wide open but not fast enough to escape his victim. New Dog was trotting right along beside him.

I could tell by the look on Grandpa's face that the battle had just begun. As luck would have it, we killed a big rattlesnake the very next day right out in our back yard. Grandpa never wasted a dead rattlesnake. I guarantee you before a dead rattlesnake was buried, someone or something would make a last acquaintance with that snake.

With a lot of planning, in which Grandpa would "give" me an idea then make like it was my own, we set out to find our victim, with the snake in tow and a ball of string in my pocket. We found him lying sound asleep in the front yard. Grandpa sneaked up and tied the string gently around New Dog's tail, then tied the other end to the snake's head. He coiled up the snake, and we quietly creeped up on the porch and sat in the swing to watch the fun.

Grandpa cleared his throat real loud and New Dog started to stir. By habit, when he was caught sleeping he would get that sheepish grin on his face, then start wagging his tail. Finding his tail wouldn't wag properly, he looked back to see what had a hold of it and saw that dead rattler coiled up ready to strike. He jumped sideways from a lying position about five feet. Of course, the snake jumped after him, landing at his side. Being sure he was in the process of getting snake bit, he took off running around the yard, hollering like a kicked dog, his rear end trying to pass his front.

No matter how fast he ran he couldn't get away from that snake. New Dog decided the only way he could escape was to jump the board fence out front. On his first try he didn't jump high enough and hit the top board head-on. The snake flew up and hit him in the rear end. Thinking he had been bit for sure, New Dog started yelping in a pitch so high it would hurt your ears. He made one more pass around the front yard with his snake, and this time he cleared the fence by over a foot and landed flat of his belly out in the road with the snake wrapped around his head. Feeling his only defense left was to stand and fight, he went at it. Me and Grandpa later agreed we had never seen such a wild and vicious battle. Finally, the string broke and he was last seen rounding the field at the end of the lane, headed for parts unknown.

Grandpa went out to the road and picked up our dead comrade and we buried him out back in our snake graveyard. I said a few words over his grave as Grandpa suggested, while he bowed his head and said the amens.

A few days later we were sitting back up on the porch in the swing and Grandpa told me he had seen one of them dog newspapers down at Crossroads Store. He said one of the ads read:

"Guard dog. Will work for room and board; several years' experience. Prefer chicken farm, no snakes."

ⓉHE ICE MAN

Before electricity, or before affordable refrigeration, there was the ice man. Back then, the ice man became the butt of an untold amount of jokes ... like the one where the husband comes home in the middle of the day. Finding his wife washing dishes, he sneaks up behind her and slaps her on the rear end. She responds: "Just leave twenty-five pounds today, Joe." I don't know if these things really happened or not, but the ice man was always welcome and had the run of the house on his triweekly visits.

Our ice man's name was Stacy, one of the friendliest people I have ever met, though very bashful. Grandpa could just mention any part of a woman's anatomy in front of him and he would hang his head and turn red as a beet. Needless to say, we rarely saw Stacy in his natural form.

59

Wednesdays were not very exciting during the summer, with school out and the crops not ready to harvest. And as it is said, "Idle hands belong to the devil." Grandpa and I had idle hands. An early morning walk around the field had produced one small rattlesnake about three feet long. As Grandpa put it, "Almost too small to kill," but we knew it was deadly to man and animal, so we did our duty and returned home with another tool that would add to the excitement of the day.

From our war room (the front porch swing) we surveyed the field of battle, searching for a worthy opponent or victim, depending on the outcome of the event. The only one that fit our bill that day was Stacy. Our weapon of choice had already been selected by the demise of the hapless rattler. Foremost in our minds now was the proper deployment of our weapon—the same as in most wars fought over the last two thousand years.

Our front gate swung outward, and a brace near the bottom supplied a perfect place to position the snake. Several trial runs proved our selection to be correct. Every time we positioned the snake and opened the gate, the snake would fall at our feet. Satisfied with this portion of our battle plan, we retreated to our observation point (the front porch swing) and waited for Stacy.

When you are involved in mischief, another developed family trait is to look as innocent as possible, even fake a kind of serious expression so you will be the last one suspected. And above all, never laugh. Any time you see one of us not smiling, look around and be very careful—you could be a victim.

Stacy's ice truck came up the road right on schedule and stopped so the load would be the closest to the gate. Stacy stepped down.

"Good morning, Uncle Redding. How is everybody doing today?"

In our part of the country, courtesies and formalities were always taken care of before business was conducted.

"Just fine, Stacy. How 'bout yourself?" Grandpa answered.

"Everything going real good, Uncle Redding," Stacy said. "And how about you, Dick Russell? You doing all right?"

"Yes, sir," I answered with my best grown-up voice and serious look.

"How much ice you going to need today?"

"Oh, about fifty pounds," Grandpa answered.

Stacy jumped up on the back of the truck, threw back the canvas covering the blocks of ice, drew his ice pick out from a holster on his side like a gunfighter, and went to work chipping off a fifty-pound chunk. Suspense built as he jumped to the ground and shouldered the ice with the tongs and headed for the front gate. I glanced up at Grandpa and was amazed at his composure. Not even a hint of what was to come could be seen on his face, just a chiseled-in-stone expression.

Stacy reached inside the gate, fumbling around until he finally found the latch. In one motion he flipped the latch up and swung the gate open. Not only did the snake fall on cue, but it landed on his feet.

"Snake!" Stacy screamed, about three octaves higher than I had ever heard anybody scream before.

Grandpa's timing was perfect. He came up out of the swing and ran down the steps with the speed of a man half his age, grabbed a strategical- ly placed hoe and began flailing away at the dead snake.

Stacy watched from his safe haven up on the back of the truck, while the block of ice and the tongs lay in the yard, covered with sand.

"Did you get him, Uncle Redding?"

"I sure did, Stacy! It was a close one. That snake could'a kilt you. Look at the size of him," Grandpa said.

"Uncle Redding, I don't know how I can ever thank you. You saved my life," Stacy said.

"Don't think anything of it, Stacy. Pick up the ice and come on out back and we'll wash it off at the pump and fix you a glass of ice tea."

When they returned Grandpa had his hand on Stacy's shoulder, still consoling him. They stopped at the gate and looked at the mangled snake. Stacy solemnly shook his head.

Grandpa looked over at me sitting in the

swing with my concerned expression and said, "Dick Russell, I want you to take a good look. This is why I don't want you running around here barefooted all the time."

Then he gave me a secret wink.

"Yes, sir," I said, looking well scolded.

After Stacy had left and we regained our composure, we set about the task at hand of having a funeral for the snake. Grandpa had me conduct the service as usual, echoing his properly placed amens.

I stopped in the middle of the closing prayer and asked, "Grandpa, do you think we ought to ask for a little forgiveness for ourselves before we close the service?"

With his head still bowed, he thought a minute and said, "I suppose so, son—we need all the help we can get."

The story circulated the community, with Stacy being the first one to know so he could join in the fun and not be the butt of the joke. Stacy passed on a couple of decades ago, but his story and his name will live for years to come. That day he became part of a legend.

WATER

I wasn't quite seven years old but I remember the night Grandpa died just like it was yesterday. The cold December air set the tone for his departure. Heavy clouds had been hanging overhead all day. Doctor Middleton had come and accomplished what he could and left to tend other patients. In his delirium, Grandpa would only allow Mama in the room with him.

He and Mama had formed a bond years ago when he had met her at a rooming house in Fort Lauderdale. She had been only sixteen and attending college nearby. To pay for her board she washed dishes and helped with the cooking. Grandpa had just completed cruising timber in the area and had decided to make a little extra money before he returned to Gum Branch by working for Florida Power Electric Company.

Mama's own dad had died when she was three years old. Although she and her sisters had been sent to an orphanage, later they joined their mother when she remarried. The stepfather treated the children as intruders; therefore Mama had never known a father-daughter relationship. The first day she met Grandpa, he became her dad.

After Grandpa returned to Gum Branch, Mama began dating a policeman, only to find out he was the son of her adopted dad (Grandpa). At the marriage, Mama had a new family.

Talmadge and I took a kerosene lamp and walked out into the cold night air to check on the chickens. As we passed the window to Grandpa's room I heard Mama crying softly and saying, "He's gone." Talmadge and I looked at each other and realized that an important part of our lives had just passed. The light from the lamp reflected off the tiny white specks floating in the air. Snow. It was the first time either of us had ever seen snow and it happened at the exact moment Grandpa died. We felt he had just given us his final gift.

As the custom in those days, the funeral home in Jesup returned Grandpa's body to our home after he had been prepared for burial. The widow had to sit up and keep vigil the first night and Grandma insisted on this right. My thoughts of Grandpa and his warmth kept me awake and I decided to go back to the living room where he was and say my final goodbye. Grandma sat in her rocking chair, wearing the same black dress she always did, except she had added a thin black veil to cover her face. Her head was tilted back, and I was jarred by the sound of her snores. Softly I walked up to the coffin and looked in and saw a stranger, cold and unmoving. I tried to say good-bye but I knew it would mean nothing now.

Without warning, Mama came up from behind and put her hand on my shoulder and almost scared the life out of me. If I could have found my voice, I would have probably screamed like a little girl and awakened everyone in the house. She took my hand and led me out to the front porch swing and covered both of us with a blanket she had brought along. We sat there and talked about Grandpa—all the good times, all the bad times, and finally the sad time that we were going through without him now. We laughed a lot and cried even more, but when it was all over, Mama and I had finally said our goodbyes—her to her chosen Daddy, and me to my Grandpa.

The damp frigid cold of the Georgia swamp winter finally blended into the warmer breezes of spring. Mama was busy as usual teaching school and Daddy had started work as a mechanic at Camp Stewart. In the afternoons I would feed and water the chickens and gather the eggs, and in the waning daylight I would go out in the woods looking for signs of a new bee tree or some of the other things Grandpa had shown me. It just wasn't the same though. I would try to remember what he had told me about different things, but when I couldn't I would feel low because I didn't have him to ask. Eventually, I walked in the woods only occasionally. The adventure had disappeared.

Heat had replaced the warm breezes as May came up on the calendar. The war in Europe had escalated and the military activity at Camp Stewart had reached a fevered pitch. Every day more and more soldiers were marching down our road. As usual, the drill sergeant would fall his men out under the umbrella of shade that our oak trees gave to allow them a short rest period. I stopped my chores for a minute and came around to the front yard, still carrying the buckets of water that had been meant for the chickens. When I saw how tired they were I did what Grandpa would have done and offered them the freshly pumped water. Their response was immediate and their gratitude was overwhelming. That night I felt that I had come back to life again and had a purpose other than taking care of chickens and gathering eggs. Plans went into motion.

The next morning I got up early and finished my chores ahead of time with an enthusiasm like never before. I found two washtubs and scrubbed them out until the inside shone, then I placed them out front next to the trunk of the biggest oak tree where they would be in the cool all day. Every downstroke of the old pump's handle brought out a full flow of cool crystal-clear water that gave me a bonus with an occasional splash on my face. Grandpa had replaced the leather valve in the pump a short time before he died and now it was going to help me become part of the war effort and fill the void he had left. Each bucket was filled half-full just like I had been doing for the chickens so they would balance me instead of trying to carry one full bucket on one side.

By ten that first morning the temperature had already climbed to over 90 degrees and steam rose from the swamp past the field in front of our house. Sweat covered the shirt under my overalls and the stench from the chicken houses colored each occasional breeze from the south.

First, I heard a rhythmic tramping sound and then out of a cloud of dust appeared the first company of soldiers around the curve in the road. As they came closer the drill sergeant counted cadence, then brought the company to a halt under our oak trees and allowed the men to fall out for a ten-minute break. They swarmed around the two tubs full of water with their canteen cups in hand and helped themselves. I continued to make trips to the pump, returning with more buckets until everyone had their fill. One of the soldiers came over to me and gave me his fatigue cap, another picked me up and put me on his shoulder, then others gave me packs of chewing gum and one, a little penknife.

Before I realized it, they had taken my new fatigue cap and were passing it around. Some put in pennies and nickels, and one dropped in a quarter. A huge sum of money! As I calculated it, three bottles of Coke and two bags of peanuts.

The drill sergeant saw my confusion with what was taking place. He came over and squatted down to my level and told me, "Son, let these men give you things and show their appreciation for the water. They are going to be sent overseas to the war in just a few days and they miss their families very much. Some of them might not come back, so let them do this. It will be almost like they are back with their own families for a few minutes." I understood completely because this was how I was filling Grandpa's void.

That night I sat at the table with Mama and we counted the money and sorted out the gifts from the day's labor of love. The thing that kept coming to mind was Grandpa telling me, "It says in the Bible to give when it is needed and you will be repaid many times over."

"What in the world are you gonna do with all this money, Dick Russell?" Mama asked.

"I don't know, ma'am," I said. "I don't feel right about getting it; I was just trying to do like Grandpa taught me."

"Well, I'll just put it in the bank for you until we decide what to use it for," she said. "But I'm telling you one thing right now, you are not going to eat all this candy and chewing gum. How about I take it to school and hand it out at recess?"

"Yes'm."

All through that summer I pumped water for the chickens and the soldiers, and when Sunday came around I missed the soldiers. Mama continued to bank the money and distribute the candy until the war was over.

Grandpa had marked the path for my life well and I have tried to follow it. The rewards have been enormous.

Thank you, Grandpa.

GUM BRANCH

Gum Branch, located in Liberty County, Georgia, got its name from the sap, or gum, that comes from the many pine trees that grow in that area. The GIs who trained at nearby Camp Stewart during World War II had other names for it ... like Camp Swampy, Little Okeefenokee, and just plain Rattlesnake. I imagine those names would seem about right to outsiders, but to people who called Gum Branch home the name represented the strength and determination of their ancestors—people who carved farms out of the swampy wilderness and made a go of it.

The eastern part of Liberty County goes all the way to the Atlantic Ocean and makes up part of coastal Georgia, about halfway between Savannah and Brunswick.

During the 1700s and 1800s the area had

great financial success. Its shipping port, called Sunbury, rivaled Savannah in trade. Rich English lords owned summer homes on large plantations. I heard they were so rich that they even bought slaves for their slaves. As a matter of fact, Teddy Roosevelt's mother made her home there, and her family had slaves. Riceboro, a little south of Gum Branch, had huge rice paddies that ran for miles through the swamps. The skeleton of the irrigation system can still be seen in the pine forest that took over when the slaves left after the Civil War. General Oglethorpe and his buddies not only had black slaves, but they also brought in several shiploads of Chinese to farm the rice. Eventually, the races mixed and all you had left were blacks with an occasional pair of slanted eyes. They called themselves "Geechies." I think it had something to do with the part of Africa they were from.

A French botanist named La Count settled just west of Riceboro and thought the humid area perfect for experimenting with plants. He had ship captains bring plants through the port of Sunbury from all over the world and introduced into this country things like bamboo and wisteria from the Far East. After the Civil War La Count moved to California and started the University of Southern California.

That's enough of the history lesson, except to say that when the British lost their slaves after the war, they took off to more civilized places where they could continue their life of silk stockings and tea parties. Coastal Liberty County kinda slipped back into the swamps, and the former slaves eked out an existence with their learned skills.

Gum Branch and other small settlements in the western part of the county continued on like before, planting their crops and taking care of their huge pine trees, which produced turpentine and lumber for the country.

I don't know what the descendants of those pioneers will eventually evolve into, but the ones I remember had the industrious drive of the Germans, the sturdy constitution of the Scotch, the blarney and shenanigans of the Irish, the talent and beauty of the Austrians, sprinkled over with a little bit of the English formality—just what it takes to build a strong community.

𝕷ANDERING

I imagine every mother and wife around Gum Branch has heard the announcement one time or another: "I'm gonna ride around for a little bit; I'll be back after 'while." It's got to be our ancestors' fault. They probably started it when they were thrown out of Austria in the early 1700s because they wouldn't join the Catholic Church. They ended up on the Savannah River in Effingham County with land grants from King George. In return, the settlers had to farm and produce food for the colony in Savannah. Even after they landed on another continent they still wandered all around.

One of our ancestors wandered around and ended up captured by a squad of British soldiers during the Revolutionary War. They killed him because he wouldn't join them. That proved one thing: the British take an invitation to join their group a lot more serious than the Catholics do. What I'm trying to say is that wandering was born deep in our soul, and when it leaves, we die.

My first road trip was called running away. I had just wanted to wander around a little, see new sights and visit people, then return home more enlightened than when I left. At three years old, though, this wasn't looked upon as prudent behavior, even in Gum Branch.

The day waxed warm, crickets sang, and sunlight glistened off the red paint on my new tricycle. It was more than any red-blooded young man could stand. I had to take it out on the open road and see what it would do. I hadn't learned how to pedal yet, but my cousin Talmadge had shown me how to stand on the rear crossbar with one foot and push with the other. This action propelled me and my tricycle to places unknown. Grandpa sat in the swing on the front porch taking a nap, and I definitely didn't want to wake him.

I checked with our old orange tomcat to see if he approved of me riding down to the next farm to see Mazie-girl, a lady who had always paid attention to me when I went with Mama. Tom said he thought it would be just fine. Matter of fact, he would just tag along if it was okay with me.

The hot Georgia sand tried to hamper our progress, but I was not to be denied the almost full-mile trip. At long last there I stood in the shade of the little magnolia tree in front of Mazie-girl's house. Tom panted little short breaths like cats do, trying to cool off, and I could feel sweat running down my legs inside my overalls. The gate was locked—nobody at home. I had traveled all this way for nothing. The only thing to do then was to turn my shiny tricycle around and head for home. Before I could complete the maneuver I heard the familiar sound of our pickup chugging down the road. Suddenly, impending doom settled over me. I had let this dad-blame tomcat talk me into doing something I shouldn't have. Now I'd have to pay for it, and he'd get off scot-free.

My first instinct was to cry. This had worked in the past on a couple of occasions. Mama proved not to be a pushover this time. She got out of the truck with a peach switch in her hand with the leaves already pulled off the branch—no cushion at all! This was going to be a rough one. I didn't speak to Tom for two or three days until he finally apologized.

About a year and a half passed until I couldn't contain my desire to wander any longer. I had traveled the woods over with Grandpa and was sure I knew every trail and swamp crossing in Gum Branch. Tom had disappeared like all big-jawed tomcats do, and "Dog," my new friend and guardian, seemed like he would make a perfect traveling companion.

Daddy was lying on the floor of the front porch sound asleep, snoring with his mouth wide open. Grandpa had gone to Ludowici with Uncle Clanton, and Mama was teaching at Providence

School. I figured I could walk through the woods and across the swamp to Harry's house and get back before anyone missed me.

Dog led the way across the back field, tail held high, nose to the ground trying to pick up a scent. His sniffing and quick change of direction was very impressive. He looked like he knew just what he was doing, but the fact was the only thing he had ever caught was a biscuit. From the top of the rail fence I could see the trail that led through the swamp to freedom.

The first footlog over the water looked a lot higher than I remembered, but I also didn't have Grandpa to hold my hand and balance me either. I had only walked about fifty feet when my foot slipped and I went face down into the swamp. The cool root beer-colored water closed in behind me as I sank below the surface. My first thought was, "I sure wish Mama could have taught me how to swim."

The sand bottom loomed up white and beautiful. I seemed to be in a kind of dream world where everything was in slow motion. A signal flashed through my mind: "SURVIVE." I flipped over and stood up. The water came up to my chest, much to my relief. Dog fidgeted back and forth on the log for a few seconds, then joined me with a splash and went dog-paddling off in the direction of the far bank. Wading along, I watched little water bugs swim in circles in front of me. I wondered if what Talmadge had told me about their ability to teach people to swim was true.

My wet overall legs made a swishing sound as I walked up the hill out of the swamp and found the trail to Harry's house. (Around Gum Branch everything above water in the rainy season is called a hill.) Dog took several side trips into the brush. Once, he flushed a covey of quail and came running back with his tail between his legs—some bird dog! By this time my overalls had dried and were starting to chafe, but I wasn't going to let that little bit of discomfort spoil my trip.

Cousin Loyall's farmhouse stood tall, its weathered siding a monument to three generations. This house had first belonged to my great grandparents, Charles and Rebecca Groover; it was the place Grandpa had been raised. Handed down to Great Uncle William, the house had then gone to his daughter Willie. She had married Jim Simmons from Ludowici and they had raised their children there. In the late thirties or the early forties, the bank foreclosed on a loan and it was put up for auction. Cousins Loyall and Thelma came back with their family from Kansas where Cousin Loyall had been working and bid for the farm.

Harry was sitting under the edge of the house playing in the fine sand that never gets wet, the best kind with which to make imaginary roads. Without too much fanfare I joined him in clearing a site for new construction. Everything was going along just fine until Cousin Thelma came out of the kitchen and looked under the house.

"Dick Russell, what in the world are you doing up here?"

"Mama sent me up here to borrow some soap." It was the best lie I could come up with, but I should have known better, for even though Cousin Thelma was a college graduate, she still had her common sense and knew right off I was lying.

"There ain't no way in the world your mama would let you come way over here all by yourself."

Time to start crying. Through my tears I looked over at Harry and saw he was crying, too. Guilty by association.

Daddy stopped the truck down the road out of sight, but not out of earshot, and gave me a spanking I still remember. Dog lied and told him he tried to talk me out of the trip, but when he failed, he felt he had to come along to look after me. There he was, sitting up in the back of the pickup, his ears blowing in the wind, looking smug and playing the hero. One of these days I'm gonna' tell everybody how those quail scared him half to death. Daddy stopped just before we got to the house and spanked me again so I would be crying good and hard when we got home, and the fact that he was sleeping when I left would be overlooked. It worked.

Here it is fifty-five years later and I still wander around. Sometimes I get up deep in the night and drive out on the dirt roads here in the Croom Forest, (my own Gum Branch), turn out the headlights, and let the full moon show me the wonders of the dark: deer grazing, raccoons hunting for food, all being watched over by a big hoot owl.

SCHOOL BUS

Mama said I was born February 3rd, 1937, just as the school bus drove by at 3:15 P.M. I have a feeling the reason that blessed event occurred at that moment was because Mama hurried so to catch the school bus each day that she had me conveniently so she wouldn't be late.

My first memory of one of these huge yellow carriers of human cargo was when it came to take my mother away and bring Aunt Hattie to take her place for the day. It has been said my feelings were so mixed that I cried and smiled at the same time.

Every mechanical vehicle, so rare in those days, was known by its own personal sound. Grandpa would be sitting in front of the fireplace looking at the paper and say, "I think I hear Clayton Hodges' Dodge truck coming. He is supposed to be at work. I hope Louise or one of the girls ain't sick." And sure enough, if you waited, that old red Dodge pickup would appear, coming down the lane in a cloud of dust. Our school bus had a special pitch to its sound, a combination of whining gears, rattling tin echoing in its own expanse, and the hum of that Chevrolet engine.

Ford families like us, as rare as that was in those days, would enter this vile vehicle hoping others of the same gender wouldn't see us.

Before Pop Tarts or other breakfast fast foods were invented Grandpa had their predecessor. He would take a freshly-baked, warm biscuit, turn it up on the end, and with his little finger poke a hole down in it. Then he would pour syrup into the hole. If he reached the proper depth, the syrup would fill the biscuit and not leak out. On those running-late days, I got on the school bus many a time with one syrup biscuit in my hand and another one tucked safely in my top overall pocket for seconds.

Winter in Georgia would take its toll, and the combination sand-and-clay roads mixed with a little rain would reach a consistency that was amazing. If you stopped on the soft part, you would slowly sink down as if you had found quicksand. On what seemed to be the more stable clay sections of the road, it would turn into something that resembled a greased plank. I have seen a truck sitting still without the engine running slide sideways into a ditch just because a farmer leaned against it while he talked to his neighbor.

Our school bus driver was an artist at his job and it was very rare for us not to be at school on time every day. According to where the bus driver lived, I was either first on the bus or last, never in between. I either had too much of a seat choice or none at all. One day when I was last to be picked up, I sat by a neighbor about my age. The winter rain was freezing almost as soon as it hit the dirt road and we were just barely making progress. The bus had no heat and the insides were exposed bare metal. Ice had formed on parts of the floor and along the lower sides.

I realized my seat companion was crying softly. "What's wrong," I asked. He said in a pain-filled voice that his foot was frozen to the wheel well beneath our seat. We took his coat off and covered his foot to warm it up, then worked it until it freed.

This might be hard to believe in this day and time, but back then it was not uncommon for a child to have either a coat or a pair of shoes, but not both. I was one of the lucky ones.

My first accident happened on that old 1937 Chevrolet school bus. It was during the war and everything was either rationed or unavailable. The tie-rod ends on the bus needed to be replaced, but because of their scarcity, wire had been wrapped around them several times in hopes that would hold them in place until the parts could be found. We were on our way home from school, clipping along at about thirty miles an hour, when all of a sudden the bus veered sharply to the right, jumped the ditch, and came to rest on top of several small pine saplings. The next thing I remember, I was standing outside watching all the other students get off the bus. I asked my cousin Guy what had happened. He told me just as soon as the bus came to a stop, I climbed out the window and was the first one on the ground. I knew then for sure I had survival instincts.

Other memories of the Georgia school bus were a mixture of good and bad. I remember my cousin George courting his girlfriend in the back of the bus and warning me if I turned around to look back he would kick my butt. I also remember making the mistake of telling him and his wife about it years later, just to be told by Joann that she wasn't his girlfriend back then.

Then there were all the games that were played to pass the time. If you saw a red truck and didn't have your fingers crossed, bad luck would haunt you and someone could pinch you. There was the one where you had to guess how many army trucks were in the convoy coming toward us; the winner had the closest number. Young boys would bet their daddy had more farm acres in cultivation than yours and their fields could get more bushels of corn per acre.

Of course, all of this was one-upmanship and outlandish numbers would be revealed. The worst times on that school bus happened when my mother and father were separated and preparing for a divorce. I stayed with Uncle Clanton and Aunt Janette at their house full of my cousins. I was in a growth spurt and my pants weren't. Every day I would get on the bus with an extra long-sleeve shirt, because before I got back to Gum Branch that afternoon I would have to tie the sleeves of that shirt around my waist to hide the rip in the seat of my pants. That evening Aunt Janette would sew them up and we would start all over again the next day. The teasing was almost unbearable.

My cousin Talmadge drove a school bus while he was still a student. I admit this sounds kind of unusual, but let me tell you the circumstances. At that time in Georgia you could get a chauffeur's license when you were eighteen years old. A lot of farm boys who completed high school were older than that simply because farming came first and school later. Social promotion didn't exist. If you hadn't completed the required work, you remained in that grade. It took an awful lot of discipline to stay in school and graduate.

A natural at driving, Talmadge would never tire. Sometimes after school he would run the bus route, then return to school and pick up the boys' and girls' basketball teams, drive them several miles to another town, play as a guard in the game, drive the team back to school, get home after midnight, then get up the next morning at five o'clock and start all over again.

Today, when I step into one of these huge yellow machines I'm covered with a wave of nostalgia and wonder what memories are still lurking, left behind by its former occupants.

DON'T EAT CHICKEN

Chicken has always been the mainstay in the country diet. A preacher's ability to convert a congregation of sinners tied directly to his reputation as a chicken-eater. Judgment came from his bone pile. A finicky eater surely could not have the best interest of God and man at heart. Even though he might praise the cook's accomplishments, the short bone pile told the truth. But if you have a preacher who stacks bones higher than his ice tea glass and accepts the last piece when offered, you have a man that can be trusted. He's hiding nothing, and you can be sure he will bring you back up out of the water when he baptizes you.

I can see where chicken farming in modern times wouldn't be too bad if something could be done about the stink, but back in the days before we had electricity on the farm I truly feel a farmer was a masochist if he raised more chickens than he could eat. Many times when I sat in church and listened to a fire-and-brimstone preacher, the only way that I could get a proper mind-picture of hell was to imagine that I had died and been sentenced to spend eternity on our old chicken farm. I feel the thought of that very possibility has kept me from straying too far from the straight and narrow most of my life, though I will admit certain temptations made the chicken farm not look that bad.

At our peak we had 1,000 White Leghorn chickens that were laying. This could be broken down to five chicken houses; 1,000 nests to gather eggs, thirteen snakes curled up somewhere in those nests (eating eggs); twenty-five watering stations that had to be cleaned, rinsed and refilled daily, and twenty-five feeding stations to clean and fill. One hand pump, centrally located, supplied the water for the five buildings. One bucket held enough water to service one station. Feed was distributed by buckets, and eggs were collected in them. Even to this day I view a common bucket the same way I view a rattlesnake.

Saturdays were what Mama called the culling day. To me it was a new form of hell. She would walk through the chicken houses with a wheelbarrow, looking for molting chickens. When she found one, she would grab it by the head, wring its neck and throw it into the wheelbarrow. I would fill two #2 washtubs full of water (by bucket) and tend the fire built under them while waiting for my first load of carcasses to be plucked. The smell that comes from plucking feathers from a dead chicken has to be experienced—it's too difficult to describe.

After they are plucked, the chickens are dipped into the second tub for rinsing, giving off a new stink all its own. Mama would inspect my work and, if it passed, she would gut the chicken, then cut its head off, rinse it one more time and throw it into a tub of chipped ice. On hot summer days Mama and I were both known to have thrown up three or four times before the job was completed. And people still think I'm weird because I don't eat chicken. Maybe some day I might be able to. It took me thirty years to start eating eggs again.

Chicken farming did have its lighter moments, though. When my cousin would come over, I would sneak a bucketful of eggs and we would play war in the field behind the barn, using the eggs for hand grenades. After the first time Mama caught me, I learned to go back and cover up the eggshells after the battle ended so there wouldn't be any evidence.

When Mama wasn't working we would take the eggs to Fort Stewart and the stores in Hinesville on Monday, Wednesday and Friday. Outside of going to school this made me one of the most traveled kids in Gum Branch.

About three times a year we would purchase baby chicks to raise into producers. On one of

these trips back from the train station in Ludowici
I convinced Mama to let me ride in the back of the
pickup, where I could help hold the cages of biddies as she maneuvered the sand beds through
one section of the road.

There I sat, thinking I was doing something
important, when all of a sudden the truck swerved
and flipped me over the side. I remember watching
the rear wheel turning just before I hit the
ground, then all hell broke loose. The world
turned into a swirling mass of white, then black.
When I stopped rolling everything spun around
above my head. I tried to stand up but my feet
wouldn't stay under me and back down in the hot
sand I would go again. The world finally stopped
spinning and I realized that I wasn't any worse for
the wear except I had sand all over me—down my
overalls, and in every crack and crevice of my
body—and Mama was disappearing down the road
in a cloud of dust, with the cages of biddies still
piled high on the back of the pickup.

I thought about crying (I figured that is what
most seven-year-olds would do), then I realized
that for crying to be effective you must have an
audience. The only things around me were pine
trees and buzzards, so my tears would be wasted.
I brushed off what sand I could and started heading home while the abrasive in my overalls went to
work. The hot sand had just started to fill my
shoes when I saw the most beautiful sight you
could imagine—our old pickup appearing up the
road in a cloud of dust. Mama got out and

checked me over. We both decided this was the time to cry.

Our chickens were sold to Cousin Lowell when Mama and Daddy separated. I didn't miss them even for a second. I knew that with those chickens added to his larger flock he had to have the biggest chicken farm around. My cousins would be having all the fun I had enjoyed, for they were living on a farm that didn't have electricity either.

I learned much from the chicken farm experience. First, there is an easier way of making a living than farming. And second, no matter how hard you work and how much you produce, sooner or later the neck-wringer will come your way.

"Lest We Forget, Lest We Forget"

IN MEMORIAM

Herewtih are given short Chronological sketohes of a number of Liberty's soldiers of the Confederacy and of some others who are in some way identified with the county.

These were gallant men, true to themselves, their fellowmen, their country and their God.

All of these whose names and records are given here now sleep their long last sleep—they have all laid down their arms and look down with fond affection upon their loved ones here who thus show to the world that they are proud of "those who have gone before," the tender and loving memory of whom they will always hold most sacred.

Well can it be said of them as soldiers, citizens and fathers:

"They fought a good fight,
They kept the faith."

The sketches follow:

S. D. BRADWELL
First Lieutenant
Enlisted August 27, 1861
Was promoted to Captain
Was wounded at Dallas in 1864 and again in battle of July 22, 1864. Was with the command at the surrender.

WM. H. RYON
Private
Enlisted August 27, 1861
Promoted to Sergeant.
Served during the war. Lost a leg at Kennesaw Mountain June 10, 1864.

S. S. MARTIN
Died January 14, 1900
Private
Enlisted October, 1861, and re-enlisted April, 1862. Served through the war until the surrender. Was paroled at Hillsboro in April, 1865.

JOHN G. RYON
Private
Enlisted April, 1862.
Was captured at Brier Creek, Ga., and held until the close of the war. He was discharged in Atlanta in 1865. Died at his home January 15, 1897.

S. B. RUSTIN
Third Lieutenant
Enlisted April, 1862
Was promoted to 2nd Lieut. He was severely wounded in the Noonday Church fight June 20, 1864, and did not go back into the war. Was discharged in Savannah, April, 1865.

JAS. M. CASWELL
Private
Enlisted in 1861 and re-enlisted in April, 1862. Was promoted to 1st Sergeant. He served through the war with his command, and was discharged in 1865. He died at his home in Hinesville in 1920.

HAMPTON C. PARKER
Born Apr. 29, 1825 Died June 11, 1902
Enlisted in Altamaha Scouts, Co. I, 25th Georga Infantry, Wilson's Brigade, Aug. 14, 1861. Served in State Senate.

WILLIAM HUGHES
Captain Liberty Guards during war His horse was shot from under him at the battle of Noonday Church which disabled him for a time and paroled at Hillsboro, N. C., April 26, 1865.

CHARLES G. GIRARDEAU
Enlisted May 15, 1862, in Co. B., Liberty Mounted Rangers, 20th Georgia Battalion, captured at Cold Harbor, Va. 1864—Died in a Northern prison.

JOHN E. GIRARADEAU
Enlisted Oct. 1861 and re-enlisted in 1862 in Liberty Guards. Killed in action at Aiken, S. C., 1864.

JAMES D. ZORN
Born Oct. 23, 1834 Died June 13, 1914
Enlisted Co. D., 5th Georgia Cavalry Volunteers, Capt. Wm. Hughes and served the entire war.

MALACHI JOHNS
Enlisted May 17, 1862, in L. I. Troop 5th Georgia Cavalry. Wounded once and was at the surrender.

In Memory of
ROBERT LONG, SENIOR
Born in 1818
Enlisted at beginning of the war in Altemaha Scouts, 25th Georgia Regiment. Served in this Company and in other branches of the service durng the war after which he returned to his home, where he lived until his death, Nov. 27th, 1893.

In Memory of
D. B. M. SHEPPARD
and
MARIAN FRASER SHEPPARD

In Memory of
L. BERRY HENDRY
Died March 1891
Christian, Soldier, Patriot

ANDREW R. DEAN
Born June 14, 1831 in South Carolina Died Nov. 28, 1918 in Georgia.
Company E, 11th Regiment S. C. Infantry. Captured with entire Company near Richmond June 3, 1863.

JAS. M. SMILEY
Born Oct. 3, 1832, Died June 11, 1904
Enlisted April 1862 in Liberty Guards, Co. D., 5th Georgia Cavalry, and served thru the war.

SERGT. JOHN A. MARTIN
Born Sept. 12, 1832, Died Oct. 4, 1904
Enlisted in Liberty Guards Co. D., Capt. Wm. Hughes, and served with faithfulness to the war.

WILLIAM DeLEGAL BACON
Born September 29, 1828
Served on the coast of Georgia, Mississippi, and upper Georgia. Was promoted to Quartermaster. Returning to his home in Liberty county

CAPT. J. MADISON SMITH
Born 1823—Died 1892
Was elected Lieutenant of the Altamaha Scouts and later made Captain Serving thru the war, was wounded once and surrendered at Greensboro N. C., April 26, 1965.

MARTIN SULLIVAN
Enlisted Aug. 14, 1861 in Altamah Scouts, Co. I. 25th Georgia Infantry Volunteers, Capt. G. T. Dunham, under whom he did valiant and honorable service.

JACOB S. KICKLIGHTER
Born Nov. 27, 1844—Died July 8, 1917
Enlisted Oct. 1862, in Liberty Guards Co. D., 5th Georgia Volunteers. Captured Sept. 1864 and held at Camp Chase until end of war.

ROBERT W. LONG, JR.
Born Nov. 8, 1845 Died Jan. 27, 1910
Enlisted May 17, 1862 in L. I. Troop Company G., Capt. W. L. Walthour. Served during war and until surrender Died at Bay View, Ga.

WM. D. BAGGS
Born 1837
Enlisted April 1862, Co. D., 5th Georgia Cavalry Volunteers. Served during the war and died July 3, 1901.

J. L. SHAW
Born Feb. 8, 1832, Died Dec. 31, 1898
Enlisted in Altamaha Scouts, Aug, 14, 1861, wounded at Chickamauga and discharged 1864.
Tax Collector 1864

JOHN E. WAY
Born July 3, 1832, Died Sept. 1, 1922
Enlisted in Altamaha Scouts Aug. 14, 1861. Served thru the war. Died in Savannah.

JOSIAH LAW FLEMING
Enlisted in L. I. Troop, May 1862 and served with distinction thru the war. Was on detached service at time of surrender. Died 1891.

HENRY McGILLIS
Born June 3, 1825—Died June 3, 1885
Enlisted in the L. I. Troop Dec. 23, 1862 (Co. G., 5th Ga. Cavalry.) Captured April 1865. Paroled same month at Newport News, Va.

ENOCH V. MARTIN
Born 1837—Died April 23, 1910
Co. D., Liberty Guards, 5th Georgia Cavalry. Enlisted Oct. 1861; re-enlisted 1962; in hospital 1864; detail duty to the end of the war.

L. L. VARNEDOE
Enlisted in Liberty Mounted Rangers May 15, 1862, promoted to corporal and then to Quartermaster and served to end of war. Died in Thomasville, Ga.

SAM'L H. ZOUCKS
Enlisted April 1862. Served during the entire war and was paroled at Hillsboro, N. C., April 26, 1865. Died in Savannah, August 2, 1904.

ORIGIN OF THE DAUGHTERS THE DAUGHTERS
OF THE CONFEDERA

KITCHENS

A farmhouse kitchen is about as special a place as can be found anywhere. It's the place that brings families together and sometimes the only place a prayer is said all week except in church.

Our kitchen wasn't like the ones you see in the movies or on TV. It started out as a log home for the family while the big house was being built—a custom back in that part of Georgia.

After the main house had been completed, a porch or walkway connected the two. I have heard several reasons for this. One: the woodstove was a bad fire hazard and if the kitchen caught fire, you might be able to save the big house. Another reason: both buildings were usually made of logs and the kitchen was a lot warmer in the winter when it might be almost impossible to heat the big house. But I believe the sentimentality of what happened in the kitchen made the difference. It was the place where most children were born and where the family bonded closely together in their early years of struggling to make a go of life.

The kitchen held their security. They didn't have the heart to tear it down when the new house up front was finished, so the older building was usually turned into a kitchen with a dining room and pantry.

The walls in our kitchen were covered with newspaper that had been dipped in a solution of water and flour to hold them in place over the cracks between the logs, providing insulation. I can remember Grandpa walking around holding up a kerosene lamp with one hand, reading the news on the wall for the umpteenth time while he waited for supper to be served. I remember getting a swat on the rear end from a switch that had been properly selected from a peach tree in the back yard when I poked a hole in the newspaper with my finger just to prove to myself I could find the cracks between the logs behind the newspaper wall.

The wood cookstove had its own room. This huge mass of cast iron never rested. Hot coals were always banked somewhere in its depths, waiting to be brought to flame by fresh pine stove-wood fed into a little door in front. Hot water wait-ed in a tank on its side to be added to washpans or tubs. At full throttle when too much wood had been added, the stove would rumble and creak, belching fire out of every crack and vent it could find. The damper on the stovepipe would bang as it swung back and forth trying to get enough air into the fire.

Mama would sprinkle water on the red-hot surface, trying to cool it down, and holler to me, "Dick Russell, run outside and watch the sparks and make sure they don't land on the roof."

I knew the importance of my job. If sparks landed on the oak shingles there was a good chance the roof would catch on fire. Then we would have to climb the ever-present ladder and sling water on the fire from a dipper while standing on the top rung holding a full bucket in the other hand.

Mama never stopped. She taught school, worked in the welfare office in Hinesville in the evenings, and issued the war rationing stamps in-between. Every weekday morning, the schoolbus would stop to pick her up and Aunt Hattie would get off to take care of me and my grandparents in her absence. I don't know how old Aunt Hattie might have been or even her last name, but I remember she was black, soft and warm with the smell of fresh soap and good food always about her person. After the evening meal was prepared and before the school bus came to take her home, she would hold me in her lap and tell me stories of long ago. Her stories kept my interest, the creak of the rocking chair singing a lullaby. The hum of the school bus would break the spell and Grandpa would take her place as we watched her depart.

Mama would return late in the evening with

the last workers from Camp Stewart, sometimes in a car, often in the back of a pickup, once in a log truck. Right away she would busy herself fixing the table with the food Aunt Hattie had cooked, usually my favorite: black-eyed peas with rice and stewed tomatoes, followed by homemade sausage and the best biscuits that the Lord would allow to be made in Georgia, that is except for my Aunt Janette's.

The Second World War brought new people to our kitchen. Uncle Sam asked the farmers who lived close to Camp Stewart to take in at least four government workers per household as boarders. As a favor, the government came out and sprayed us, our farms and our water supply with DDT. A week later, a crew of men dug a big square hole in the back yard. Then the next day a big truck delivered us a brand new double-hole outhouse made from rough-sawed lumber, guaranteeing at least two splinters per visit.

I don't remember the boarders' names, but I still see their faces. Three spoke in an unfamiliar manner; Grandma warned me not to get too close because she thought they might be Yankees, or at least have some Yankee blood in them.

Supper, a special affair around the long table, was lighted by what folks called an "Aladdin's lamp." Although shaped like our old kerosene lamps, the metal bottom held a mantle instead of a wick and gave out a bright light.

Grandpa sat at the head of the table, the four boarders on a bench to one side, Grandma, Daddy and Mama on the other side. I sat right up to the table in a tall chair, making me a part of everything. Every night, the boarders would give me a penny. One night one of the boarders apologized because he had only a dime. I promptly jumped down and brought him change.

Conversation around the supper table was always a big part of our lives and included everyone. I will never forget one such occasion. I asked Grandpa what the word "f---" meant.

The room became quiet, then came a little snicker and a few muffled coughs. With his usual grace and calm, Grandpa asked, "Where did you hear such a word, son?"

"From Miles," I answered after a little thought. Although young, I knew anything bad could be blamed on Cousin Miles.

Grandpa cleared his throat and said, "Dick Russell, that is a word that describes something ... we'll talk about it after supper."

"Yes, sir," I said. "Will you please pass me the f------ potatoes."

One boarder spit a mouthful of tea across the table, another started choking on a biscuit. The other two jumped up from the table and ran outside, laughing. Daddy kept on eating, Grandma and Mama held their aprons up to their faces, and Grandpa passed me the potatoes. After supper Grandpa explained the word to me in such a manner that I never used it again.

Several years later, I returned with my dad to the old abandoned log kitchen to tear it down. It had to be dismantled one log at a time. Each log had been hand-drilled and put together with wooden pegs. I thought of the care my Grandpa had used as he built the structure and my task became very solemn. The newspapers on the walls inside were stripped off one layer at a time. They revealed our local history from the <u>Liberty County Herald</u> and <u>Savannah Morning News</u>. Reports from the war in Europe awoke feelings of sadness. When someone from Gum Branch was killed or missing in action, the whole community gathered at the family's home, bringing food and special things to comfort them. We mourned their loss way into the night.

As more layers were stripped away, I found a memorial to those who served in the Confederate Army. It read: *James D. Zorn, Born Oct. 23, 1834 Died June 13th, 1914. Enlisted Co. D 5th Georgia Cavalry Volunteers, served the entire war. Charles A. Groover, Lieutenant, served with Remshart and was present at the treaty signing at the Appomatox Courthouse. Died 1873.*

Very carefully I took a pocketknife and removed the delicate piece of family history from the kitchen wall. I could feel Grandpa's presence and the warmth of his smile as I folded the newly found treasure away and went about looking for more archives on our old newspaper wall.

OLD PET

L ike most farmers, we had a mule which supplied the plow power to till the fields and plant
the crops. She also served as alternate transportation, whether we were riding bareback or she
was pulling a wagon or a sled. I thought the good
Lord had blessed us because we only had one
mule and not two, like most farmers.

The U.S. Government even used the mule as
a means of measurement. To constitute a farm
you had to have forty acres and one mule. I don't
know whether or not if you had more than forty
acres you were punished by being required to
have more than one mule.

I heard Grandpa tell Uncle Minzie one time,
"Mules are really old Lucifer himself wrapped up
in a horse hide, with long ears stuck on top."

Our mule's name was Old Pet. Whoever named her that had to have done it as a joke. My first memories of Old Pet had to do with being awakened by the sound of loud explosions, and my dad cussing as he pulled on his pants and headed out the door. Old Pet had decided she wanted to eat early so she got our attention by kicking the boards out of her stall. Yard chickens that happened to wander into the lot that surrounded her stable immediately became targets for her wrath. Ears plastered right back on her neck, eyes showing white, she would take off chasing them, snorting, braying and bucking in the air. If the chicken escaped she would back up to the fence and kick at the boards so hard it would sound like a shotgun being fired.

Cousin Miles was just a little boy when he wandered into Old Pet's lot. Mama looked up just in time to see the mule stalking Miles like a cat would stalk a bird. Mama got there just as Old Pet charged, and the mule hit her shoulder as she scooped Miles up and ran for safety. The bruise healed but it always hurt her when the weather turned bad. I remember Mama rubbing her shoulder years later, saying, "There must be rain coming—Old Pet's acting up."

A good farmer in our part of Georgia was judged by two things: how straight his rows were plowed and how many bushels of corn he could harvest per acre. The lack of a bountiful harvest could be excused because of the weather, but a crooked row fared worse than being caught with the preacher's wife. Wherever farmers would gather, whether at "Joe Long's" or "Crossroads Store," this would be the first topic of conversation during the planting season. I can remember the farmers standing around in their overalls, drinking six-ounce bottles of Coca-Cola. The accusing party would look around real obvious first to make sure the victim or some of his family wasn't in earshot, then he would start, "Did you see Earl Johnson's rows? They's as crooked as a snake."

"Naw, not Earl's!"

"Yes, sir. Just as crooked as can be. Him or his mule had to've been drunk when he laid that first row out."

Then someone else would say, "Well, I know for sure that Earl quit drinking, so it must of been his mule."

Grandpa had as straight a row as could be found anywhere. He told me the secret: tie a white rag on the fence at the far end of the field, then aim between the mule's ears just like you would aim a rifle. When you got to the fence you would have one perfectly straight row, and all the rest of the rows would fall in line and be just as straight as the first one.

Old Pet had a built-in clock and you had better be ready. At exactly five o'clock in the afternoon she would head for the barn. I don't care how much cussing or pulling on the plow lines you did, she was going to the barn—right across the rows, dragging the plow and the plower right along behind. Your clock had to be at least as good as hers, ready to quickly cut the plow loose before she left. A pocketwatch was issued to any farm help hired to break ground. Around five o'clock, we would go out to watch the fun because no one would ever believe what we said about Pet.

Mules are supposed to be genderless, I have heard, and they can't reproduce. But the only excuse for some of Old Pet's actions would probably be explained in this day and time by a mule analyst, who would say that she had permanent PMS. On one such occasion she started by kicking all the boards out of her stall, then she ran head-first through the lot fence, sending splinters flying. Next, she chased a young calf around the yard until it got walleyed. Pet stopped and we thought it was all over, then without warning she charged right towards the house. At the last second she slid to a stop, dragging her butt on the ground for more braking power. Then she turned and kicked the house with both hind hooves.

Daddy ran outside, leaving a string of his usual cusswords behind, just in time to see her tear down the front gate and head towards Gum Branch Ford. Daddy left, headed in Pet's direction in his old '37 Ford truck, and you could hear his special mule words above the roar of the engine and the rattle of the fenders as he disappeared in a cloud of dust.

About thirty minutes later we all came out on the front porch to see the commotion. There came Old Pet down the road with Daddy right behind her. He would blow the horn and race the motor, then bump her in the rear. Pet would stop and buck way up in the air and kick the front of the truck with both hooves. It was a sight I will never forget and an incident that I would pay for over and over again later. Daddy and Old Pet were both traumatized by the episode. Afterwards, every time Pet would hear an engine of any kind, she would start bucking, then head for the barn. And every time Daddy saw a mule, he would flinch and blink his eyes, like he was about to be hit. I don't know what happened between the time Daddy left and when he came herding Old Pet back. He would never talk about it.

As I grew older, the care and maintenance of Old Pet fell to me. My reward for this job was my own transportation. Bareback was the only way she could be ridden. Old Pet had set that rule a long time ago. Every time someone would put a saddle on her, she would blow up her belly and make you think you had the cinch tight. Then, when you tried to board, she would suck in and the saddle would slide around to her belly, and then she would take off, braying and bucking.

My cousin Lawrence, who has been like a brother to me all my life, lived away off in Metter, Georgia. On one of his trips to visit he introduced me to electricity, and erased all the wonder I had about it. He had me stand up on the front porch swing and told me to stick my finger into the empty light socket hanging from the ceiling. The next thing I knew I was lying on the floor with a numb right arm.

"Do you know what that is, Dick Russell?" He asked in his best instructive tone. "That is electricity."

I had learned a lesson well, but I knew that sometime or somewhere, there would be a payback. It came sooner than I thought. That same summer, Lawrence came to stay with us for a few days. I introduced him to Old Pet. We rode double, bareback, through the woods to his Aunt Thelma's house to visit our cousins. We were halfway back when I heard a pickup in the distance.

Before I could give a warning Old Pet stopped and pointed her ears toward the sound. The next thing we knew we were flying through the air like we had been launched by a giant slingshot. The hard-packed ground didn't offer much cushion, and the landing hurt. Lawrence got up looking kind of bewildered.

I said, "Lawrence, do you know what that was? That was a mule."

Old Pet couldn't be used in the picking of tobacco. The one time I remember they hooked her to a sled, she stopped between the rows of tobacco, reached over and ate a leaf. After a while she started staggering around and heaving. I know ... people have told me time and time again that mules or horses can't heave. But I will always remember that mule leaning against the fence, heaving like an old drunk.

One of my chores during the winter was to hook Old Pet up to the wagon and go looking for firewood. On one of these trips Old Pet got spooked by the wind blowing the leaves. I jumped down from the wagon and ran up beside her to grab hold of the bridle, hoping to get some kind of control. About that time, she stepped sideways and landed on my foot. Unbearable pain pinned me to the frozen ground. It didn't matter what I tried, she wouldn't remove her hoof. I used every mule cussword I had ever heard, I slapped at her until my hands hurt. I could visualize us being found next summer, a skeleton of a mule standing on the skeleton of a boy. My foot finally went numb and I could think more clearly. Old Pet liked one contact with a human—that was when her hooves were being cleaned. I reached down and slapped the back of her leg like I had seen

Grandpa do, and she promptly raised her hoof to be cleaned and, in doing so, set me free. I climbed back up on the wagon and headed for home.

My last ride on Old Pet came the day we rode over to my Cousin Harry's house to see the new pony he had just received. After all of the customary inspection of the new pony, with a lot of the good points brought out, like the shape of its back and the good condition of the hooves, he saddled up and we headed down the road to Uncle Minzie's house to see Shelby, another cousin.

We started racing. It must have been some sight—a roan-colored pony with a white blaze, and a big-butted mule the color of black death with a tan muzzle, running at full gallop. All of a sudden Old Pet's head disappeared from in front of me and I catapulted through the air and into a ditch full of mud. Harry said it was one of the most spectacular sights he had ever seen. Old Pet had tripped, turned a forward somersault and landed on her back, wild-eyed and kicking straight up in the air. No real damage had been done except I was scared out of about ten tears of my life, which I could well afford at that time, but not Old Pet, for she was already over thirty years old.

A short time later my roots were ripped out of the good black Georgia soil and transplanted in the Florida sand. Daddy sold Old Pet to Mr. Lester Wells, and Mr. Lester sold her about five years later to somebody he really didn't like. I don't think Lester Wells ever spoke to Daddy again.

ℛAISING CHILDREN

Everyone in Gum Branch felt they were responsible for the upbringing of all the children in the community. Children were allowed to run free at social gatherings because everyone knew a grownup was watching out for them. If they were getting into trouble or in a dangerous area the adults did what they were supposed to do and steered the kid in the right direction. Their responsibility didn't stop there either. I can hear Miss Illa May now. "Come here, little boy, and let me wipe that snot off your nose."

"Yes, ma'am."

"What's your name?"

"Roger, ma'am."

"Well, Roger, here is something to clean your nose with. Now go and play, and keep away from that highway over there."

"Okay."

"What did you say, young man?"

" Uh, yes, ma'am."

"That's better."

And so it went anywhere in the community. The safety and security children feel in this kind of enviroment is comforting, to say the least. They know their boundaries. So, until they reach the age of mental responsibility they are free to be kids.

Being the community schoolteacher gave Mama more responsibility for everyone's children, and she met the challenge well. Her little schoolhouse was in the community of Providence, now incorporated as Gum Branch. The real Gum Branch is on down the road west of there about three or four miles. It's kind of confusing how the name changes came about. I haven't figured it out myself yet. Mama taught the first through the eighth grades in the proverbial one-room schoolhouse. Most of the time she fixed lunch, too.

Mama believed that children learned better with a good hot meal under their belts. She would start off the morning with assignments for all the grades that would keep them busy until their turn came to be up front for their lessons. The first grade was taught reading from a huge book which was placed on an easel. Next came math on the chalkboard, then spelling. After that, they were assigned printing and writing of the ABCs with the help of an eighth-grader. The second-graders then moved up front and were taught their subjects and given their assignments. This rotation continued throughout the day.

The younger kids would overhear the lessons of the older kids, and pretty soon they became so advanced that they were way ahead of the students in the city schools. Mama believed that any child in her school should be able to pass a test for a high school senior when they completed the eighth grade. It was a cruel fact that many farm children were not allowed to go farther in their education.

Mama didn't have time to put up with discipline problems, so they were dealt with on the spot—once with a warning, the next time with a switch on the rear end right in front of the class. By the time I was ready for the second grade Mama sent me to the school in Hinesville, "The Bradwell Institute." Isn't that a scary name? Anyway, she said it was for my own safety, for she feared I might be maimed because she had to switch me so often.

Any child who had a medical problem was looked after right away. Dr. Welbourn from Hinesville would stop by each week and look the kids over. Once a year they were checked for worms, and at one time or another every child had them. First, you were given this humongous pill to swallow, about the size of a Luden's cough drop, then the next day Mama would give you a dose of castor oil. On the third day you were worm free, and clean as a whistle. A note was sent home to let the parents know what was going on. Mama said if she took time to convince the parents that their child needed medical attention there would be a good chance some of them would have died of hookworms. I think Dr. Welbourn and Mama split the cost of the medication.

Once, Mama visited the farm of one of her students and saw his baby brother with sores all over him. She thought back to some of the classes she had attended at Georgia Teachers College (Georgia Southern) and realized that these were syphilis sores. She went straight out to the field and confronted the farmer with the problem. He told her that until that child became of school age he wasn't any of her business, and if she came back around butting in, he would run her off with his shotgun. Mama told the farmer that the child wouldn't live long enough to get to her school. He repeated his threat.

Mama being Mama, she went straight to Dr. Welbourn and told him of the situation. Together with Sheriff Paul Sikes, they returned to Providence and took the child from the farm at gunpoint and had him admitted to the hospital in Savannah. There, he was given a series of treatments until he was cured. They explained to the rest of the family that they had been exposed to a disease and they had to be given shots, kind of like for smallpox.

The farmer stayed closer around home after

that and didn't visit the camp followers any more. Before he died several years later he came to our place and thanked Mama. Knowing country people I realize how much courage he had to muster up to do that.

Before I came along, there was a second-grade student in Mama's school who was at the head of his class. Come the end of the school year, she failed him.

She took the student home that day and sat down and had a talk with his parents. It seemed that this child was extremely brilliant but was goofing off while he made the best grades in the class. When given harder work he would play dumb and say he couldn't do it. The mother and father both knew that their child would take the easy way out and they backed Mama whole heartedly.

The kid was devastated. Mama told him that when school started if he applied himself and did the kind of work she knew he could do, she would promote him to the third grade with the rest of his class. Come the first week of the school year he was transferred to the third grade and never looked back again. In World War II he was placed in military intelligence, and after the war was over he followed the Russians home as a spy and lived there for five years. He retired from the Pentagon as a colonel.

Christmas brought cold weather to the little schoolhouse and gave the children new responsibilities. The older boys had the task of finding enough wood to keep the little potbellied stove in the middle of the room perking. The older girls were put in charge of instructing the younger children in the fine art of making decorations. I can still see the paper chains, glued together one link at a time, stretching all the way across the room, and still smell the aroma of the pine boughs that hung over the windows.

Mr. Hinton Mobley, who owned most of the land around the school, would come over and take the students on a walk through his woods to find a Christmas tree.

Each person was given his own right of approval in the selection, and when the choice was made, an eighth-grader was given the honor of cutting the tree down. Back at the schoolhouse, Mama was waiting with hot cocoa and homemade muffins to warm everyone. The rest of the day was spent setting up the tree and decorating it with all the homemade decorations. The only store-bought decorations that I can remember were these four huge shoe-shaped things that when unfolded became crepe paper bells and were hung from the ceiling. Mistletoe hung in the doorway during the season, and occasionally some boy would get up enough nerve to see if it worked.

The parents were invited to the play that was given on the last day of school. Farmers in overalls would come in freshly scrubbed with their hair slicked back and sit on the benches with their families while the miracle of the Christ Child was played out on the stage. Once, Mama put the play on with real animals, but it took us most of the Christmas vacation to clean the place up.

After the play was over and Coca-Colas were passed around, Mama would make her entrance dressed as Santa Claus with a sackful of gifts. Earlier in the week Mama had everybody draw the name of a person to whom to give a gift. The gift had to be handmade because a lot of the families didn't have money to buy food, much less a present. Each gift would be inspected by Mama and if it didn't come up to par she would assign one of the more talented students to give a helping hand. The best-kept secret of World War II had to have been who had drawn whose name. I have never seen anything taken so seriously in my life. But that was great because the anticipation brought the excitement of gift-giving to where it should be.

Santa Claus would reach down in her bag, pull out a gift, and announce "For Novadine from Wilber." Silence would fall over the schoolhouse, except for the sound of the footsteps on the wooden floor as the red-faced Novadine came forward to get her gift. Just as soon as she took the gift from Santa Claus, the silence would be broken with applause and laughter. The first round of gift-giving was on its way, with Santa Claus trying to be heard over the commotion.

I will never know how Mama did it, but she would always save up enough money over the year to buy each child a special gift from Santa Claus, too. I also remember that some of the parents were called up to get a gift from Santa Claus. Most of the time it was just a small envelope. Now all Mama had to do was get ready to put on the Christmas play at Gum Branch Church, with Santa and a Christmas tree, and then prepare Christmas at home.

Aunt Janette did more than her part in raising children around Gum Branch. They would gather around, hoping to be the object of her affection, even if it was only for a few minutes. Here was a woman so full of love that words fail me when I try to do her memory justice. The best I can do is wish every child could experience being the third one to crawl out of a number-two washtub that still had the same water in it that the previous occupants used, and stand there buck naked in the chill of the evening while Aunt Janette rubbed you down with a fluffy towel. When you were dry, she would give you a stinging pop on the rear end with her hand, and a big bear hug that let you know beyond any doubt that you were safe ... and loved.

No story about Gum Branch and children can be told without mentioning the matriarch, Edith Matilda Long Groover, known as Aunt Eddie, Grandma, or Mama. I haven't ever heard her called anything else. She was Grandpa's brother Hamp's wife. Aunt Eddie and Uncle Hamp had ten children, and when Uncle Minzie's wife died in 1913, she took on the responsibility of mothering their six children right along with her own. It's no wonder that the Groover family reunion originated at her house, and for years was held there before being moved to Gum Branch Baptist Church. When Mama and Daddy were separated for a while and I was kind of passed around the community, I felt more at home at Aunt Eddie's than anywhere else ... after Aunt Janette's.

Aunt Eddie was famous for telling it the way it was. One time a family member came to her home with a baby who was dirty and needed his diaper changed. Aunt Eddie took that baby from her and told her that she wouldn't let her have the child back until she could care for him properly. The mother, who was known to be a fighter fisted up for a minute until she realized that Aunt Eddie was ready to put her life on the line for the health of this baby. That child grew up and became a decorated army officer, and in civilian life a top executive in one of the largest companies in the country.

When I die, and if I get to heaven, I expect to see Aunt Eddie sitting there in a rocking chair comforting and rocking the latest tiny arrival.

GUM BRANCH BAPTIST CHURCH

Gum Branch Baptist Church was established back around the 1850s by the ancestors of the people who still live in the community. The original building wasn't a whole lot smaller than the new chapel; the only improvement over the years was adding a front porch. When the congregation built the new building, instead of tearing down the old one which held so many wonderful memories, they just moved it to the back. They stored memories in the new masonry building before they finally tore the old church down.

Somewhere in the history of the church there was a dispute in the congregation, which is common to Baptists. Half of the members moved across the road and started the Liberty Baptist Church. I can only remember being in that church once when we went to a revival over there, even though my first cousin Louise married Clayton Hodges, the preacher's son. All during the week I would visit Louise and play with her daughters Ollis and Marilyn. Come Sunday, I believe we weren't even allowed to speak to each other.

Most of the time our services with a real fire-breathing, Bible-pounding circuit preacher came on the first and third Sundays of the month. Grandpa told me that one time they had a preacher who came out into the field where he was plowing to preach to him about his sinning, and he was using a live rattlesnake for a book marker. Now that's a tough preacher.

The sure way to go to hell back in those days was playing cards. Next was drinking beer. (I'm glad it wasn't moonshine or there wouldn't have been any deacons left at all.) Then there were the picture shows. Mama would take me all the way to Glennville so I could see a movie and, sure enough, some other church member sat in the next row over. The secret to success here was not to acknowledge that you had seen each other. Dancing was the makings of the devil himself. It was so forbidden that just the thought of dancing became erotic. You couldn't go swimming on Sundays, and if you bought anything at a store it had better be for medicinal purposes.

I remember one time we had a baptism on Sunday after the services at Buck Horn Ford. The weather was so hot that you could hardly breathe. All of a sudden, Talmadge fell off the bridge and landed face-first down in the cool water. Before you knew it, about half the congregation jumped in to save him. I think his brother Miles might have pushed him. The preacher said as long as the waters were already blessed that it probably wouldn't hurt if everyone else cooled off, too.

One time they had a dance at Theodore Wells' farm. It was kept a big secret so nobody would get in trouble with the church. There was Daddy's cousin Ernest, a deacon, playing the fiddle, my great uncle Johnny Zorn and his wife Uila playing a fiddle and a mandolin; Mr. Frank Long furnishing the refreshments; and Daddy doing most of the dancing. I had a front row seat to the entertainment, sitting on a hundred-pound sack of seed peanuts with a hole in it so I could help myself. The next day in church everybody acted like they hadn't seen each other all week.

Gum Branch Church was way ahead of the times. We had electric lights powered by an old gas generator and a row of open-top, wet-cell batteries. Liberty Church only had gas lanterns that hung from the ceiling, hissing. Daddy never got thrown out of the church for all his hell-raising because he kept the generator running. At Sunday night meetings the preacher would be going strong, rattling the rafters, and all at once the engine would start to sputter, the lights would flicker and go out. Daddy would get up and fumble his way outside to the little building that housed the generator. The congregation would be just as quiet as a mouse, then you would hear some girl giggle. Over on the other side some boy would get his face slapped, then everyone would laugh. The preacher would clear his throat real loud and calm everybody down. You could hear Daddy turning the crank, talking to it.

"Dad damn tunndabitch, crank up, you sorry tunndagun!" There would be snickers and more giggles followed by a few mammas' "Shhhhhh." Finally the engine would sputter to life and the lights would come back on. Daddy would walk through the door with grease up to his elbows, looking like nothing happened, and the preacher would ask for an "amen" for Brother John T.

Years later I found out why Daddy slurred his cusswords even when he was sober. He explained that you weren't really cussing if you didn't say the words right.

Mama taught Sunday School and started putting on Christmas plays with the children at church. At first she had a lot of resistance from the deacons, but somehow their children always seemed to have very important parts in the play.

On Christmas Eve Mama would get somebody to cut down a big holly tree with red berries on it to set next to the pulpit. She and all the young girls would decorate it with just about everything.

Then, when everybody was in church, she'd come in dressed like Santa Claus, in red longhandles with white cotton sewed around and a cotton beard, carrying a big flour sack full of presents on her back. The little kids would sit in amazement, with their mouths open. Santa would call each child up by name and give them a present of some kind that was gift wrapped. That gift was chosen special. Times were hard, so this might be the only thing that they would get for Christmas.

Mama was Methodist. I'm sure it was kept a secret by her and Daddy, because Methodists were known to go to picture shows and drive Chevrolet cars. Both were looked upon as sins in Gum Branch. When Mama passed away in 1985 I contacted a Methodist minister to conduct the services. I figured since they had paid her way through college down in Ft. Lauderdale and given her a job until she graduated at age seventeen with honors, she was obligated to remain a Methodist. All my Baptist deacon cousins came down to attend the services and pay their last respects. Everything went along smoothly until the closing prayer. The preacher ended the prayer as only Methodists do with, "Forever and ever, Amen." They looked up so quick that you could hear their necks snap, and I'm sure Mama was looking down, laughing.

Singing was always a big part of the community and it all originated in that church, I don't care what they say over at Liberty Baptist. I had forgotten what a beautiful sound came out of Gum Branch until I returned years later and heard my cousin Lindell and his daughter Cheryl singing. On one occasion I brought a friend with me who had a professional music background to a family reunion. He sat in amazement as Miles' daughter Delores and son Fred sang a duet and he couldn't believe they didn't have formal training or even know how to read music. Then Cheryl, with her strong alto voice, sang an old gospel song, backed up by her family and Jimmy Moody. Finally, cousins Maurice and Nelda's daughter Carol sang a solo while she accompanied herself on the piano. Here was a young teenager who played baseball with the boys and was tough enough to stand her ground with anybody—what we called an average Groover girl—but when she sang I'm sure that the angels in heaven even stopped to listen. Her voice was so delicate and pure that I can only describe it as the sound a violin string would make if it was spun from the purest gold. My friend sat there with tears flowing down his cheeks. Cousin Connie's children closed out the singing with "Amazing Grace" inviting everyone to join in. Later outside, my friend asked why I didn't sing during the closing number. My wife smiled as I explained to him that I had promised not to sing if they would let me come to the family reunion. He thought for a second and said, "I've heard you sing and I think that's a fair trade."

A lot of things have happened to me since I left Gum Branch, but the people in that church and the teachings that I received there gave me a background that kept me from wandering off too far in the wrong direction and gave me someone to call upon in a time of need when no one on earth could help.

TRUCKS AND CARS AND THINGS

Prior to and during World War II the main mode of transportation around Gum Branch was mostly horseback, mule and wagon, and by foot. I've read reports of ways for us to exercise so we can be healthy, and realize that poverty is the answer. Although we weren't considered poor by Gum Branch standards, we just hadn't come up to the standards of the rest of the country. Once my generation decided what we thought we wanted, we went out and got it: big air-conditioned homes without front porches, nice clothes, appliances that we could throw away when they broke, and enough food so we could waste a little now and then. Not to mention the almighty gas engine trucks, cars, motorcycles and tractors. We even had to grow grass so we could buy gas lawnmowers. At one time it was a disgrace to the housewife if she had grass growing in her yard. Instead, the ground was raked clean of leaves, and patterns were made in the fresh dirt by the rake tines. Some of them were quite outstanding.

Riding all day on a tractor, even though it's hard work, doesn't compare to following behind a plow drawn by a mule for pure exercise.

Mr. Dowse Smith had the first tractor around and come spring he would hire out to cultivate the fields of those who didn't have enough children to do the plowing. The last time he plowed our field there came a rain that turned the ground into a sea of mud. That tractor stayed stuck up to its hubs for two months. A monument to technology. Our mule, Pet, would have gone to the barn at the first sign of a sprinkle, dragging you with her. I can't ever remember seeing a mule bogged down in mud—maybe a horse, but not a mule.

The tractor increased production to the point that it almost paid for itself. Of course, more land was cleared for planting to produce more crops so you could buy a better tractor that cost more money, and the circle continued.

Country people walked everywhere in those days, and if somebody stopped by to visit, you were glad to see them because you knew they had put out a real effort to visit you. It wasn't just a spur of the moment thing to do.

Grandma told me that one time they had a mailman back after the turn of the century who delivered mail on a motorcycle.

Ralph Groover went to Fort Lauderdale after he got back from the First World War and became a motorcycle policeman and rode until he tangled with a wet railroad track and ended up with a broken back. He was on up in years the last time I saw him. There he was, standing beside his field with his dog, almost blind from a radiation treatment for skin cancer. I drove up and got out of the car to tell him who I was when his dog jumped into the back seat and started licking my son and daughter in the face. Before I could say a word, he said, "I don't know who you are, but my dog tells me the kids in the back seat are Groover younguns, they're the best smelling young'uns in the world." That was a great welcome home.

Around 1950 I rode an old Harley to Gum Branch and watched a mule who thought the motorcycle was a demon drag a farmer across a rice field, braying and kicking all the way home. I left that Harley there for two months and almost everybody in the community learned to ride it.

Trucks were mostly used for what they were designed for and held no real status in the community like they do now. I know for sure that if you even thought of putting a load of manure in the back of a new-style designer pickup you would be placing your life in jeopardy. Of course, there are still a few real farmers left who actually haul things in their trucks.

I was taught to drive at age seven like most of the other farmboys who had something available to drive. I learned to drive in the same old '37

Ford pickup I was thrown out of in Hinesville when I was three years old. They said I reached down to pick up my hat and accidentally opened the door. I tumbled out the passenger side and rolled across the street into the front door of the Hinesville Ford Company. Daddy said it was a sign, so while I was being tended to he went in and tried to make a deal for a new truck.

After Cousin Maurice came back from the war he bought a log truck and went into business hauling pulp wood. I can still remember his brothers and myself all sitting in the front seat side by side, driving that truck. Talmadge would steer, operate the clutch and brake. Connie would sit way up on the front of the seat and operate the throttle. My job was the gear shifter. Miles, sitting on the outside, instructed. Talmadge would start off in low gear with Connie pushing on the gas. Talmadge would push in the clutch, Connie would let off on the gas, I would put the gearshift into neutral. Now this is where it gets tricky. The old truck transmissions had to be double-clutched, that is, while shifting you had to go to neutral, let the clutch out, pat the gas pedal twice, push the clutch back in, then shift into the next gear.

I never was very coordinated, and it showed up here. I would try to shift either too early or too late, and the transmission would let out the most horrible grinding sound imaginable. Miles would start instructing. "Boy! What in the world is wrong with you? You gonna strip that transmission slap out'a the truck!" Then everybody would start telling me what to do all at once—kind of like the way the IRS is run now. Maybe that's why I qualified for government work later in life.

Anyway, the learning experience was worth all the confusion and the memories are beyond value. Cars were the status symbols. They were strictly for show and excuses abounded for reasons to buy one. We still find excuses to buy new cars.

Grandpa had a Model A Ford that constituted a real problem for him. He knew how to drive a Model T, with all the pedals and levers on the floor, but the new gearshift pattern on the Model A—basically the same one that is used even now—baffled him to no end. I imagine the fact that he was almost eighty years old had something to do with it. Mama drew him a diagram of how to shift gears and taped it on the dash, but it didn't help.

One time while he was trying to figure which pedal was the brake he ran into the side of Gum Branch Baptist Church and almost knocked a block out from under the foundation. His last trip in that old car landed him waist deep in Gum Branch Ford. He said that headlights from another car blinded him and he drove off the bridge. I can still see him sitting wrapped up in a quilt in front of the fireplace. He handed Mama the key and said, "Louise, I better quit driving before I kill somebody." I believe giving up his independence was the hardest thing he ever did.

Daddy's whole life was cars—well, besides partying and drinking. Until the day he died at seventy-eight years old anything automotive had his full attention. I even had an engraving of a Model A put on his tombstone—I'm sure he would have wanted it that way.

Daddy's reputation as a mechanic and a driver was known all around, and if you were ignorant of his ability to drive and rode with him, you probably got out of the car and vowed to never to ride with him again. One challenge he gave himself was to see how close he could come to cows and hogs that used to roam freely on Georgia highways. He had a points system. At sixty miles per hour, if he could clip the cow's tail and she did not look up, that was ten points. If the cow looked up but didn't move, that was five points. If the cow looked up and ran off, that was minus five points. Usually this game was played with a new passenger in the car and a few drinks under his belt.

In 1945 new cars became available for doctors and a few more special people. Daddy had already gotten dibs on Dr. Middleton's '42 Ford business coupe over in Ludowici. I think part of the deal was to never carry me back to him again to get something sewed up or a bone set. I was known for being a bad patient.

Cousin Connie and I were cruising around one Saturday afternoon in the '42 Ford (I was ten and he was nine), and we stopped by Buck Horn Ford to see if anybody was in swimming. There were the Smileys with their Fords and the Moodys with their Mercurys. After a little tire kicking we all headed back. I was in the lead and planned to stay there.

Just past cousin Ernest's place I hit a sand bed and lost control. That Ford went sideways into a high bank, then up on two wheels and back down on the road. I looked over at Connie and he wasn't moving. I don't know to this day whether he hit his head and was knocked out, or just in shock. Daddy's tools from the car and his old Spanish War pistol were strewn up and down the road. We picked up the tools and straightened out the bent left, rear fender and headed home.

The first thing I did when we got there was to go straight and tell Daddy what had happened. He started cussing about the bent fender but cooled down when I offered to pay to get it fixed. The next thing that he was concerned about was if I was in front of the rest when I wrecked, and how far. He wasn't going to have me shame the family name by being behind anybody. He never did ask if Connie or I were hurt. All that driving experience paid off years later when I was on the Tampa Police Department. Another Georgia boy, Pete Saunders, and I ended up teaching pursuit driving and trained the motorcycle officers to ride.

Daddy taught Tracy, my first cousin (that's the one my youngest son was named after), to drive. Tracy's over seventy now and still has those quick reaction times that can hardly be measured. When I ride with him I just try not to watch where he's going. Back when he was eighteen and home on furlough before being shipped overseas to the war in Europe, Mama made sure he had gas ration stamps to fill his tank. I don't think that

too many people knew that Gum Branch Baptist
Church ration stamps helped Tracy have his last
fling before shipping out. Mama said, "The Lord
would have wanted it that way." After he got back
from the war we waited all day on Uncle Clanton
and Aunt Janette's front porch for him to get
home. About three o'clock in the afternoon we
heard a car coming from way off. You could tell by
the sound it was what we use to call "flying low."

"That's Tracy," Talmadge said.

"If it ain't, it's got to be one of the Moody
boys," Miles said, "'cause Uncle Johnny's here."

Through the pine trees you could see a rolling
cloud of dust coming. When he reached the clearing of the field we could make out it was a car.
Then the prettiest maroon Mercury convertible we
had ever seen, with a white top and white sidewall
tires, slid sideways and came to rest up close to
the front fence. Tracy was home.

Over the years the fast cars and the faster
driving paid off—sometimes for the good and other
times not so good. On one occasion—I think I was
about fourteen—Daddy and I came back to Gum
Branch for a short visit. As usual, I drove and
Daddy sat with a case of Tropical Ale between his
feet on the floorboard. Most of the time we made
the 300-mile trip before half of the ale was gone,
sometimes we didn't. There wasn't anything to
worry about, though, because he always had
another case in the trunk.

That night, my cousin's wife and I finally

talked her husband and Daddy into going over to the Cherokee Restaurant in Midway for a shrimp supper. We ate shrimp until Daddy and Cousin got embarrassed to ask for any more, even though they had just about finished the last case of Tropical Ale. On the way home Daddy and Cousin serenaded us with "Red Sails in the Sunset" and "Baa baa, I'm the Black Sheep of the Family," then out of the dust loomed Grady Shumans' juke joint. There wasn't any talking them out of it, we just had to stop.

Well, one thing led to another, and this great big paratrooper made a pass at Cousin's wife and Cousin asked him to step outside. They went to the front door—which didn't have any steps down from it—and Cousin beckoned this big red-headed, bull-looking paratrooper to jump down on the ground first. This gave Bull all of the advantage, he thought. He was probably planning to catch Cousin with an uppercut as he jumped down.

What he didn't know was that Cousin was one step ahead, and when Bull turned to slug Cousin, he got kicked in the face with a combat boot. Bull fell back a little, then smiled. Cousin uttered those famous last words, "OH, SHIT," and the fight started in earnest.

Have you ever noticed that in an all-out bar brawl, there is what I can only describe as a designated screamer. That's some woman screaming about three octaves above high C: "Oh, my God, they gonna kill him." I've heard it many a time, and I wonder if they have to practice those high notes, or are they just natural?

Somewhere in the middle of all this, John T. (Daddy) made it out to our little green Ford and got a mechanic's favorite weapon—one of the biggest ball peen hammers you have ever seen. Back inside, Cousin's speed and agility had kept him one step ahead of Bull. John T and ball peen made their move. With one blow to the forehead Bull went down to his knees. I don't have any idea how it happened, but the next thing I knew, there was Bull standing in the middle of the floor with Daddy's ball peen hammer, swinging it over his head, and people were jumping out of windows and pushing their way through doors. Bull was all alone. If he wanted to fight somebody, he was going to have to go outside.

He must have known that '50 Ford belonged to Daddy because he ran over and started busting out windows. Finally, somebody distracted him long enough for us to get in the car and leave.

As I pulled out of the parking lot we saw Bull and three carloads of paratroopers loading up to take off after us. The chase was on. I hadn't been moved from Gum Branch very long and I knew every turn in every dirt road around, so I had the advantage. The only thing that gave any problem was the wind coming through all the windows that were broken out. That is, except the one little piece of the driver's windshield that still had Daddy's hammer stuck in it.

The chase didn't last long, and I heard that Bull was arrested the next day with this huge knot on his forehead and the judge, probably another cousin, ordered him to pay for the windows in Daddy's car.

Those were the good times. One of the bad times was when cousins Miles and Luther collided on a curve out past Louise and Clayton's farm. Both were hurt bad and their cars demolished.

Miles went on to become the chief of police in Hinesville. In the Liberty County sheriff's department he set state records for drug arrests that still stand today. Luther went on being Luther, because nobody could ever play that part better than him.

The Moodys had their own driving reputation. Mr. Will Moody and his wife, Wilbertha, their sons, Carlos, J.C., Dupree, Joyce, Billy, Jimmy and Dan, and their daughter, Joann, were moved from their farm by the government when Camp Stewart was built. They resettled west of Gum Branch Church and became a respected part of the community. Anytime you saw the Moodys they looked like they had just been bathed and scrubbed. I know they farmed because I saw the crops. If I had money back then I would probably have paid to see a Moody dirty.

Joann told me that even in the summer her mother would stand in front of the fireplace with a roaring fire going to keep the flatirons hot, ironing white long-sleeve shirts for the boys and Will to wear on Saturday and Sunday. Thirteen of them, and she would put them on the back of chairs first because if she put them on hangers right away they wouldn't hold their shape.

One reason they fell right in with the rest of Gum Branch is because they all drove Fords or Mercurys. I heard that later on one of them went to work for Chevrolet. We won't mention his name, though, and bring disgrace to the family.

The roads around Gum Branch twelve miles in any direction were choking dust to impassable mud, according to the weather. The Moody boys had black cars with whitewall tires, and these cars were spotless anytime you saw them—never even a haze of dust. After church on Sundays, especially if it had been raining, we would go out to see if their whitewalls were muddy. There wasn't even a speck. We figured they knew Moses personally and he had parted the mud for them.

I know their cars were driven and driven hard because all the little kids used to walk down to the curves of the dirt roads and try to figure out whether it was a Groover or a Moody that last went by, according to the way the dirt was thrown up. We were so accurate we could almost tell the name of the driver by the berm he left. Matter of fact, I didn't know that all dirt roads didn't have banked turns until after I left.

Times have changed, though, and almost all those dirt roads are paved over now. But I still see that same challenge and abilities in their grandchildren. The Moodys are still spotless, and a lot of the Groovers went into law enforcement. After all, somebody has to catch all those reckless drivers.

TOBACCO, SYRUP, PEANUTS & POLITICS

For years tobacco was the primary crop in the south. South-central Georgia has a different way of curing its tobacco than most of the rest of the country. It's strung on five-foot-long, one-inch square sticks, three leaves at a time and tied secure. Then it's hung across tiers inside the tobacco barn and cured or toasted by heat that comes from huge pipes which are on the floor of the barn. Without electricity, fuel-fired furnaces or thermostats, it became quite a chore to get the perfect finished product, especially when the farmer had to depend on wood, but the finished product paid extremely well. The heat was brought up to a constant 100 degrees, then raised two degrees per hour until it reached about 185 degrees. It was kept at that temperature until all the stems on the tobacco leaves were brittle and would snap when you bent them. After you reached that point, you extinquished the fire in the long furnace. The barn doors and vent windows were opened to allow the leaves to cool and collect moisture so they wouldn't be so brittle when they were handled. Even though I haven't smoked a cigarette in over twenty years I can tell right away when somebody lights up a Lucky or a Camel and that toasted aroma floats through the air.

Gathering tobacco and curing it usually became a social event. Field help were paid four dollars a day. For that four bucks they would stay stooped over all day, picking off the bottom three or four leaves of each tobacco stalk. When an armful had been collected, the leaves were laid with the stems pointing all in the same direction in a high-sided sled lined with croaker sacks, drawn by a mule that would go and stop by voice command. When the croppers got ahead of the sled, someone would call out "GIDUP" and the mule would pull the sled down the row until they called out "WHOA" and then the mule would stop and wait for instructions. A good mule moved on her own when needed. We never had one like that.

Some young boy would ride the mule bareback as it pulled the sled to the barn and would help unload the leaves onto long tables in front. There the handers (two or more per stringer) would pick up the leaves by the stem, three at a time, and hand them to a stringer who wound the string around the stems twice and around the stick once. When the stringer filled a stick up she would call out "STICK" and a little kid would bring her an empty stick and take the full one into the barn. The barn help would stand braced between the tiers all the way up to the top, sometimes as high as forty feet, and would hand the stick of tobacco up from one to the other until the last man would hang it in place across the tiers. It wasn't unusual for the temperature to reach as high as 130 degrees in the barn while they were working. Every once in a while you would hear a commotion, then a loud "Whomp." Somebody had just slipped and fell in the barn. Whatever happened, you could never admit that you passed out from the heat—only sissies did that.

Outside barn help and handers were paid two dollars a day, while stringers and barn workers got three dollars a day. Of course, you usually didn't get paid until the tobacco was sold. Before lunch break the croppers would ride up to the barn with the last sled of tobacco from the field and start washing up for lunch. This always led to a lot of muscle-flexing while they took off the long -sleeved shirts they had to work in and changed into something clean. Of coursed the young ladies would giggle and pretend to be duly impressed.

Sometimes after lunch couples would pair off and sit in the shade and talk until they had to go back to work. I remember one time we were working tobacco at Cousin Loyall's farm and his sister Annie Pearl came with her family. The youngest boy, Lynn, worked with me in the barn while his two sisters handed tobacco. Grace, as she was named, was quiet, pretty and graceful. Her older sister Joyce was almost the opposite—outgoing, good-looking and full of devilment. During lunchtime Joyce put on a show with her trick bicycle riding skills while wearing shorts and almost drove all the guys crazy. The really bad part was that they couldn't say a word because they were all related to her.

Toward the end of the day, the stringers would usually start a little competition to break the monotony, and whoever could string the most sticks of tobacco over a certain period of time would be held in high esteem throughout the community, kind of like a gunfighter, until some-one beat her time. The croppers would come back up in the evening with the last sled loads, wash and change shirts, then tease the young girls until it was time to go home.

Being old enough to sit up all night and keep the temperature just right while the tobacco cooked was kind of like a passage into manhood. It meant you had reached the age of responsibility and could be trusted with the outcome of a very important money crop. The first night Connie and I were allowed to watch over the tobacco being cured we expected the worst from Miles and Talmadge. In Gum Branch it was the sworn duty of older boys to scare the young barn-watchers on their first night. We were prepared with a gas lantern and flashlights. Everything went along smooth until it was almost midnight and our apprehension had reached its peak. From behind the barn, where the lantern light didn't shine, came this loud mournful scream. We stood there frozen in place, hair standing up on the back of our necks and chill bumps cropping up all over.

Connie looked at me, saying, "That's the boys ain't it? Sounds like a panther, but it's the boys."

My response sounded doubly bad. Not only did I stutter normally, but now I was shaking so bad that I couldn't keep my voice an even tone. "It's Miles," I screamed in a high pitch. "He-he-he k-k-k-k can sound just like a panther."

After I got that out we seemed to be a lot calmer. We even took the flashlight and shined it out in the woods and told them we knew who it was and they could come on in now. No response. So we gave them a few more minutes and extended our offer again. This time it was met with another scream and a lot of bush-shaking.

That was almost full proof to us that our guess was right. We were going through a "little brother" initiation. They never did show themselves, but off and on they would let out a blood-curdling scream just to keep us awake. At dawn the next morning Miles and Talmadge came walking up to check on us. We met them with a big, knowing grin and commended them on their performance. At first we thought they were carrying their act a step further. We told them about our visitor that night and, of course, they thought we were just kidding, then Talmadge found some big cat tracks that eventually disappeared into the woods. Since it was too late to be scared now, we played the part of the fearless tobacco barn-watchers right up to the hilt with a lot of spitting and scratching. I don't remember us ever sitting up at the tobacco barn again.

Cooking syrup came under the same category as curing tobacco, with the staying up all night and keeping the fire just so. Cane grinding wasn't near the social event as tobacco harvesting, but it had its moments. Sugar cane grows from parts of stalks that are saved from the previous year. The sprout comes out of the joint and puts out roots, then produces a long corn-like stalk. Some of the cane that farmers planted around Gum Branch had direct ancestry back to the 1700s and I have never tasted any sweeter juice or syrup anywhere. Years after I had last sampled some of Uncle Clanton's syrup I thought that the flavor was just my imagination and they all tasted the same. That is, until I went back to visit and tasted his syrup and Aunt Janette's biscuits, with thick, fried bacon on the side. I feel the combination can get you about as close to heaven as you can get and still be alive.

Farmers try to cut cane in the fall before the first frost. This keeps it from being bitter. Those same tobacco sleds are used to transport the cane to the mill, where it is squeezed by these steel rollers and the juice flows down to the collecting barrel. One of the job benefits is having all the cane juice you can drink. The other is to take a little of the foam and juice off the top and set it aside. The sugar content is so high that before you know it you have what they call "skippy," which is a potent rum-like drink that will guarantee you two things: a hangover and diarrhea. But while it's working it sure is fun.

The juice is poured into a big cooking boiler that is about six feet across and the bottom slopes down on all sides to about two feet deep in the center. The secret to good syrup is steady heat, just a little over 130 degrees for about forty-eight hours, and constant stirring with a big wooden paddle about the size of a boat oar. The person cooking pulls the paddle up every few minutes and checks the color of the syrup and the thickness. Being the cane syrup connoisseur that I am, I find that the best syrup has the same deep auburn color of Gum Branch swamp water and is just about twice as thick.

Once the syrup cooking process starts it can't be altered in any way, so a lot of preparation has to be made, including having enough wood to finish the cooking, an extra paddle, a gas lantern and a kerosene lantern for standby, and a good night's sleep. One person usually takes the full responsibility for the outcome.

About the last time that Miles cooked he got himself into a situation that could have ruined over a hundred gallons of syrup. Somehow the thermometer got broken and there wasn't a spare. Miles didn't hesitate for a second. He stuck his finger into the syrup and counted as high as he could until he couldn't stand the pain any longer, then pulled it out. This way he had some kind of idea how hot he would have to keep the syrup until it finished cooking.

Every twenty minutes you would hear, "One two, three, four, five," in rapid succession, then, "Oww, that's hot." Just before he ran out of fingers the syrup was finished. Uncle Clanton said it was the best batch he ever turned out.

Peanut boilings were the biggest social event that surrounded that same cooker. The fire was built early in the day, and people would come from all over to dig peanuts and pick them off the vine. At least five boxes of salt were put in to start with, and others were added as needed. Then the socializing would begin. Somebody would always turn a conversation into a story about something it reminded him of a long time ago and it would mushroom from there. One after another had a tale of their own to tell. Every once in a while, somebody would say, "I got to walk around a little and stretch my legs." This was a sure notification that it was time for another drink.

There was, and still is, a standing rule around Gum Branch that you don't drink in public, and I guess that's pretty smart in several ways. First, you don't have your wife or anybody else counting how many drinks you have had. Second, it creates a camaraderie among the participants that gives an outsider a chance to fit right in. One of the highest honors was to be invited out back.

As the evening progressed and the peanuts were just about done, gallons of iced tea would be brought out. I don't mean just iced tea, I'm talking about nectar of the gods that would put a diabetic out with the first sip. We rated tea just like the manufacturers rate oil. The good stuff would be so sweet and thick it was called "forty weight." As the quality dropped down so did the rating. Unsweetened, which was five weight, was just for old people and sissies.

Everybody looked forward to peanut boilings except mamas. Not only did they have to contend with their iced tea being rated, they had to try to keep an eye on the old man and see how much he was staggering, and they had to look out after their daughters, too. Since electric lights weren't available yet, as darkness fell over the gathering couples would slip back into the shadows and get better aquainted. I can still hear those mamas trying to keep track.

"Shirley ... Shirley, where you at? Answer me, girl."

"Here I am, Mama."

"You don't sound like Shirley—come up here in the light and let me see you."

There would be a lot of shuffling and somebody would break in with, "Did I ever tell you about the time ...?" Somewhere off in the distance you could hear bare feet running on hard ground and Shirley would appear in the firelight.

"Where you been, young lady, and how come your face is red?"

"Mama, I wuz just sitting over there eating peanuts."

"Don't give me none of that, where's George?"

"Here I am, Miss Johnson."

"Shirley! What you doing with grass all over that new dress?"

"Honest, Mama, I wuz just sitting over there eatin' peanuts. Just ask Carol and Jack; they can tell you that's what I wuz doing."

"Where's Carol?"

Shirley had just sold out her sister to keep her mama from questioning her further.

"Carol ... Carol."

And so it went on through the evening.

That syrup boiler played an important part in the political world also. I remember the time that Herman Talmadge was running for governor of Georgia. He did his politicing over at Rye Patch, down the road from Mr. Douse Smith's farm. The day before, Daddy and Uncle Clanton took me and Talmadge with them and went up to help start the cooking. When we got there Old Bartow, a black man who lived in the community, was chopping wood for the fire. Men were sitting around, cutting up pork and chicken. Some of the housewives shucked green corn and shelled peas. The conversation drifted from one thing to another until it landed on the object of the gathering. Would Herman make as good a governor as his daddy, Eugene? After much discussion the majority agreed that as long as old Eugene stayed alive he would keep young Herman in line, so everything would probably be all right, and if he did happen to die, Senator Russell could look after Herman until he served out his term.

Politics might not mean a lot to some people, but in Gum Branch it was just as important to pick the right candidate as it was to decide what crop you were going to plant that year. Talmadge and I were both in an unusual situation. If either one of the state of Georgia's top political figures messed up, we would be ruined for life. He was named after Eugene Talmadge, the governor, and I was named after Richard (Dick) Russell, the senator from the great sovereign state of Georgia. Every time he would open his mouth in a speech over the many years I would hold my breath, because somehow I knew if he messed up I would carry the blame. Don't ever name your child after a politician who's still in office.

Toward midday, gallons of water, tomatoes, corn, carrots, hot peppers and any other vegetables that were available were added to the meat that had been simmering, and the cooking process started. Not unlike syrup, the stew had to be stirred constantly and the heat watched all the time. Since most women didn't vote they weren't expected to put out too much of an effort in the preparation. As night wore on farmers would come up and take their turn "spellin" Bartow with his cooking. Of course, there was always a jug floating around somewhere. There's something I bet a lot of people who read the new history books don't know: back in the '30s and '40s there were more black voters registered in Liberty County than white.

By noon the next day Old Bartow and the Brunswick Stew would both be about finished. I can still see him standing up there, his eyes blood red from no sleep, stirring that mixture with his wooden paddle. Cooked just right, the stew couldn't be eaten without a glass or two of iced tea to quench the fire. Those politicians were pretty smart back then, too. You had to listen to the speech first, then you could eat.

Now let me see ... I'll get me one of those syrup boilers and build a brick furnace under it. I'll run for county commissioner first, then ....

CAMP STEWART

In the late thirties the government figured it needed an antiaircraft training area. It looked all over the country and decided that southeast Georgia wasn't much good for anything else except raising rattlesnakes and alligators, so it went in and bought up a whole lot of land and built itself a military reservation. Some towns it took over, like Taylors Creek and Willey, had families who had lived there for two or three generations. Even if the price for the property was fair, just the thought of being uprooted from your family homestead and moved away, knowing that the homes were going to be destroyed, must have been pretty bad. About the same thing happened in the Smoky Mountains with the Tennessee Valley Authority. That's the next thing to genocide.

Some of the people moved over to Pembroke,

others to Glennville, but most to Hinesville and Liberty County. I know that my Aunt Janette's family, the Martins, were originally from Taylors Creek. Some people even had their ancestors dug up out of the graveyards and moved. The government promised to maintain the other cemeteries.

Daddy had bid on one of the farmhouses the government auctioned off for the materials, and he had just a short time to go in there and tear it down and haul out the bricks and lumber. After that, the place would be restricted when it became an artillery range. Do you know what happens when you tell a "backwoodsman" that he can't go into an area where he has roamed and hunted all his life? That's right, it doesn't work very well.

Every Saturday or Sunday when they weren't firing those big howitzers, we would pile into the truck and take off across our land that bordered Camp Stewart and go scavenger hunting, roaming over the old homesteads looking for valuables left behind. One of the things we found was dummy shells from the big guns ... we thought.

The first Sunday, we brought back four of the big steel bullets and started making flower bed borders around Mama's Cherokee roses she had in the back yard. They were so heavy that every time Daddy would throw one in the back of the pickup, it would shake the whole truck. After four or five months we had shells all over the place, some of the prettiest borders you have ever seen.

One Sunday we had just gotten home from church and were waiting for Mama to put dinner on the table, when they broke into the war news on the radio with a special bulletin: "A family in Pembroke, Georgia, returned home from church to find that their front porch had been blown away by a mysterious explosion. It is believed the only casualty was the family dog. All that has been found so far was a collar with his name on it, 'Buster,' and a little piece of tail."

The newscaster went on to say that the dog had been named appropriately. In just a few minutes there was another break in the news broadcast. A man who was introduced as being from the War Department announced that the explosion in Pembroke was caused by an unexploded shell that the family found on the firing range in Camp Stewart, and they were using it as a border for their flower bed. He said that anyone caught with an unexploded shell in their possession would be prosecuted by the federal government to the fullest extent of the law. He ended his announcement with the report that a deaf, snub-tail dog with no collar had been found, dazed, wandering around a quarter of a mile away, and it was thought to be Buster.

The silence that filled the room is memorable until this day. Grandpa got up very cautiously and tiptoed out to the front porch to view our beautiful collection of unexploded shells. Mama and Daddy just sat there and looked at each other. Without too many words spoken, Daddy took a mattress and put it on the floor of the bed of our truck. Gingerly, they dug the shells out of the ground and placed them on the mattress. Hay was stuffed between each shell. When the pickup was loaded, we went back into the government area very cautiously and unloaded the shells.

This continued all through the day and into the night until the last load was completed just before daybreak. I often wondered why the women and children weren't taken to safety before this demolition project was carried out. The only thing I could figure was, if there was an explosion, we could all go together and there wouldn't be anyone left for the government to prosecute, because everybody knows that being prosecuted by the federal government is worse than death.

Years later while I was a policeman in Tampa, I received a call to go to a dredging company to check out an object they had dredged out of Tampa Bay. When I arrived, I found workers throwing this huge black ball back and forth. Sometimes they caught it, sometimes they missed it and it would hit the ground with a "THUD." Upon inspection I found it to be a live cannonball with a brass plate that read "Federal Arsenal - 1861." It was from the Civil War. I called the bomb squad at Mac Dill Air Force Base and stood by while they removed it to a place to be exploded. As I watched them drive away, I got that homesick feeling for Gum Branch and World War II.

When evening came, it was show time. Daddy would start a fire in an old washtub and add damp corncobs to make smoke to repel the mosquitoes. About dark, the target-towing airplanes would start flying over, pulling these huge towel-shaped targets made of white silk. The searchlights from Camp Stewart would swing their beams around in the air until they spotted one of the targets, then the fireworks started. Antiaircraft shells would light up the sky and house-shaking explosions rattled the windows. The phosphorus shell explosions were so bright that we could actually see our own shadows that they cast on the wall of our house.

This show of lights and explosions continued on into the wee hours of morning. Years later, my kids couldn't understand why Fourth of July fireworks displays never impressed me. When I tried to explain the enormous performances that I had seen regularly as a kid, I realized that you just had to be there.

Occasionally, one of the shell bursts would cut the towing cable to the target and it would go spiraling down and disappear in the woods. Grandpa would stand up and stretch to get a better view, then he would reckon just about where it landed. "That one prob'ly fell just about where the old Martin place use to be." Daddy had figured out the firing schedule and knew about when the guns would start firing again, so we would take the pickup and sneak back into the government area and look for the targets. These weren't something that were hard to miss; some of them were over one hundred feet long and forty feet wide, made of pure silk. If we beat the Army to the target, we would attack it with knives and shears and strip the silk from the aluminum frame, throw it in the back of the truck, and Daddy would drive like a madman to get back to the house undetected. We never took the aluminum frame. After all, we were patriotic and metal was for the war effort. For the next few months women would sport these beautiful silk blouses and dresses all around Hinesville and Ludowici, a huge departure from their usual print feedsack material.

Army convoys constantly ran the road from Glennville to Hinesville, which is now highway #196. The clay dust filled the farmhouses all around and covered the crops in the fields. Every once in a while there would be a break that allowed civilian vehicles to move from one place to the other. Some of the Army drivers said they drove for as much as twenty-four hours in a row without sleep. This took its toll on the war casualties, too.

There was a real sharp curve right after you crossed over Gum Branch Ford bridge. Twenty miles an hour was about the maximum speed that the curve could be navigated. Every once in a while a truck would be trying to catch up with the rest of the convoy and the driver, drowsy with fatigue, would misjudge the turn and flip the truckload of GIs upside-down right there. Often as not, one or two would lose their lives and never see battle.

Along this road where the convoys ran were

several places where clay had been dug to build up the roadbed. These huge excavations would fill with water and afford some pretty good swimming for the kids. The only other decent swimming place around was Buck Horn Ford, where we had our baptisms. Mama used to take wagonloads of young people over there on Saturdays and teach those who couldn't how to swim. That is, everybody but me. I would follow her instructions to the letter, but as soon as she would let me go, I would sink like a rock. I would watch the other kids that she taught swim all over the place while I had to stay in the shallows. The thought did cross my mind a time or two that she might not be telling me everything I needed to know about swimming.

Some people did try and swim in Gum Branch Ford, but it was only the brave. Water moccasins and alligators could be seen cruising the waters quite often. One time, Tracy and Earl Hodges, the preacher's son, went skinny-dipping there, and when they got dressed Earl had a black widow spider in his overalls that bit him. Here he was, only in his mid-to late teens, with gray hair from the spider venom just like an old man.

The clay holes were usually shallow near the road but would get as much as twenty-five feet deep towards the back. It was standard practice to skinny-dip. After all, most of the swims weren't planned. There was one thing that some of the kids would do: go under water when they heard a car coming, and when it got right at the clay hole, they would raise their naked butts out of the water. It was called "letting the moon rise." This would get a lot of reaction from the Army trucks, with soldiers applauding and hollering at us.

Years later, my daughter was driving along an interstate highway in her pickup, with her brother and a friend in the back. She noticed that everybody who passed in their cars, had big smiles on their faces. While she was thinking how friendly people had become, she happened to look in her rearview mirror (no pun intended) to see two naked butts sticking up in the back of the truck. I could only smile and remember. One day Talmadge and I were letting the moon rise when we heard a truck come to a stop. Just as quick as we could, we turned ourselves upright and found Mama standing there on the bank with her hands on her hips. The switching wasn't too bad—she had to stop two or three times to compose herself.

Remember my cousin Lawrence who taught me about electricity? Well, he was the one who finally taught me how to swim, too. We were at the biggest clay hole close to Thelmer Saulters' farm and the water looked inviting, so we went in. Lawrence started off teaching me the proper way to hold my hands when I dove--out front, with one folded over the other to make something that looked kind of like a wing. He explained in his best instructive tone, as usual, that when I dove, if I pointed my fingers up I would make a shallow dive, and if I pointed them down my dive would take me deeper.

There I was, standing up on the bank at the deep end trying to create the perfect form, when he talked me into diving in. I hit the water with my fingers pointed down, and, sure enough, I went straight to the bottom, about ten feet down, and stuck headfirst in clay mud. When I was able to free myself, I swam to the surface. Lawrence said, "Okay, let's try it again, but not so deep this time." I never did tell Mama how I learned to swim, just that Lawrence taught me.

Saturdays were always special to country people, and a visit to Hinesville, right there at Camp Stewart with all the soldiers in town, was just like going to a big carnival. Every store had either a slot machine or a pinball machine that paid money. There was also a horse race machine where you put in a nickel, picked the number of a horse, and watched while little metal horses raced down the length of the machine to the finish line. I never did win on one of those.

Talmadge was about the luckiest and the smartest player I have ever seen. He would climb up on the Coca-Cola crates that they had placed there so kids could reach the slot machines, drop his nickel in and pull the lever. We would watch the oranges, lemons and cherries fly around, and it seemed as if the machine always gave him five nickels back. He would take that money and go buy whatever he wanted, and wouldn't play a slot machine again until the next time he came to town. Another gambling game, a punch board, cost you five or ten cents and gave a chance to take a little wooden peg and punch out one of the indented places on this board. A little folded piece of paper would fall out the back. The store clerk would unfold the paper and read your prize. Sometimes it was fifty cents, sometimes a candy bar, often as not though it was "Sorry, try again."

Camp Stewart had a big effect on the education of the people in Gum Branch. I'm not talking about scholarly education, I'm talking about learning about the rest of the world firsthand. We were introduced to scam games, con artists, and the business of prostitution (I'm not talking about just some lady who had loose morals; I heard they even gave receipts, among other things). In turn, we introduced them to fishing, hunting, good cooking, and the church. Both sides survived, but we might have received the short end of the stick.

Several of the young ladies around Hinesville married GIs from Camp Stewart and moved away to live with their husband's family up north after he was sent overseas. Usually, the culture shock became just too much and they ended in a divorce before the marriage even had a chance to work.

My Aunt Ruby, Mama's halfsister from over in Jesup, came to live with us after Grandpa died. She worked at Camp Stewart and taught school at the same time. A trait that she carried through her life until she was near seventy was that she thought if you only worked one job while you raised a family, you were pretty lazy. She introduced me to weenie roasts, the guitar, tennis, and all kinds of new things. I'm not saying she wasted her time, because the companionship is a treasure that I will hold dear always. I could make better music with that tennis racket and hit a tennis ball farther with a guitar than anybody in Gum Branch.

Anyway, this goodlooking, athletic, intelligent young lady intimidated most of the eligible men around Gum Branch to the point they became tongue-tied just trying to carry on a conversation with her, much less asking for a date. One look at that red hair and those black eyes that could shoot lethal sparks on command told you right off that this was no ordinary run-of-the-mill woman. As luck would have it, though, she fell in love with this Yankee soldier from Michigan and got married. She didn't look on it years later as a mistake—I believe she called it a learning experience.

Transportation for this many people in what had previously been a rural area was quite a problem. Mr. Mingledorff and Mr. Bagley started the B&M Bus Line, which provided the off-duty soldiers with a way of getting into Savannah and other towns in the surrounding area.

After all, Hinesville could only accommodate so many people. Outside of glorified school buses they had a few special vehicles that I have never seen on the road anywhere else or have I ever read about. These were semi-buses. The driver sat up front in the truck cab all by himself and the passengers sat in a section that was made from a semi-trailer, just like the ones that haul freight even now. The entrance door was about halfway down the right side of the trailer. There were windows all around and fairly comfortable seats on both sides of the aisle. This was undoubtedly one of the most unusual and efficient means of transportation I have ever seen. Cousin Maurice drove one of these semi-buses until he went into the Army and said it was great for the driver. He wasn't bothered by the passengers when they got rowdy or drunk, and if something happened to the motor, they just pulled in another truck, attached it to the passenger trailer and drove away. They used Hoke Martin's service station in Hinesville for a terminal, just like the regular bus lines.

Little blue flags hung from almost every family's window with a star on it for each member of the household who served in the armed forces. Gum Branch, as a whole, was blessed. The only one killed in action that I can remember right off was Cousin Julian Simmons. Glenn Groover, shot down over Germany on January 30, 1944, was a flight engineer on a B-17. The circumstances of his being on that flight were unusal. A few days before, he had awakened sick and missed a mission. On that mission his regular crew was shot up so bad that the plane crashed upon landing, all the officers were killed and the rest of the crew were injured so severely they were hospitalized and sent back to the States. His first flight with the new crew didn't end that great, either.

While they were bombing a ball-bearing plant over Germany they were hit by antiaircraft fire. One shell exploded close enough to the plane to put it out of commission. Glenn was struck by over twenty-five pieces of shrapnel. He bailed out and was placed in a prisoner of war hospital, where he underwent surgery. He had so many metal fragments in his body that they couldn't get them all. He was liberated fifteen months later.

Now, every time he walks through a metal detector he gets to recall World War II. Maurice served his time in the South Pacific around the Philippines. Tracy followed the Normandy invasion into Germany and stayed until the surrender.

Ludowici [pronounced Ludo-wisee], a little town about fourteen miles west and south of Hinesville and Camp Stewart on Route 84, going toward Jesup, did its part for the war effort, too. It had been an industrious little town in the past when the Ludowici Tile company operated.

A German industrialist named Ludowici came to the area in the early 1900s and found it perfect for producing an orange roof tile made from clay. Labor was cheap, the right color clay lay in abundance nearby, and a railroad ran right through the town. I imagine that changing the name of the town from Johnson Station to "Ludowici" had a lot to do in establishing his plant there, also.

We had direct connection to Ludowici. Daddy's oldest brother, Uncle Jimmy, lived there with his wife Nina and their three children: J.D., a military man; Lewis, who wound up a member of the Atomic Energy Commission and a weapons developer; and Norma, who retired as an officer of a bank in Savannah.

When we would go over to visit we usually took Uncle Clanton with us and dropped him off at the drug store. There, he could argue politics and discuss how good our generals were doing until we stopped on the way back to pick him up. Sometimes, we would have to wait for him to finish his visit before he would leave. He loved to talk so much that once Tracy, his son, finally drove home to Gum Branch and left him there after waiting over two hours for him to finish. It is a shame that the art of conversation is just about a thing of the past now. We are either too busy or we just don't care anymore.

Ludowici had its movie theater downtown facing the railroad tracks, with the name of every county resident who served in the military painted on the side of the building with pride. When one became a casualty they would put a star beside his name. On Sunday afternoons you could find families standing there looking at the "memorial wall." Across the street sat the phone company, occupying a small brick building just down the road from the Catholic church. It just dawned on me why this little town in the South had its own Catholic church. I bet that old man Ludowici was Catholic. The only other Catholic family around was the Simmons family, and half the time they went to our church.

The main hub of activity had to be the bus station, with soldiers coming and going all the time. Local girls were known to go there just to hang out and meet GIs.

Another type of business lady, posing as a local girl, waited around, also (sometimes she WAS a local girl). The big difference between the local girl and the foreign girl was the local girl always knew the location of the booze. Long County had passed a "no alcohol" law, but was known as the wettest "dry" county in the state of Georgia.

Another distinction that set Ludowici apart was that it had to be the worst speed trap in the nation. That's right, this wasn't just some state or local recognition—this was big time. I have heard it said that people who haven't ever been in Georgia have gotten a speeding ticket from Ludowici. They would get your name and just mail them out at random. I even found a man in the little town of Sylva, North Carolina, who cringed when I mentioned that I was from around Ludowici, Georgia.

Out on the open highway coming into town, they placed the city limits sign and a twenty-five miles per hour speed limit sign right behind a state sign that read fifty-five miles per hour. Even if you happened to see it and locked up your brakes, it was too late. You could pay your fine right on the spot, but if you protested you went straight to jail and waited for a trial. At the trial you would be found guilty and charged two or three times the amount of the original fine. The government sent the FBI in one time to investigate. The Secretary of the Treasury had to go out and sell extra war bonds just to get their agents out of jail. The AAA routed people around the whole county just to miss Ludowici.

When Jimmy Carter became governor of Georgia he had the road department put up signs on all the highways leading into Ludowici, warning the public of the speed trap. That calmed things down a lot, but I don't take any chances when I travel through there even now, and I advise everyone else to use caution, too.

I can say one good thing about Ludowici during the war: there was a little place on the right side of the bus station that sold the best hot dogs I have ever eaten. GIs would stand in line to pay ten cents for one of them. The weenie was longer than the bun, and the bun was a little on the sweet side and always toasted just right. I don't know if they made their own catsup and mustard, but I know I haven't found anything that tasted just like it since.

After the war Ludowici flourished for a little while, then dwindled down to just a few buildings. Hinesville, on the other hand, continued to grow. Camp Stewart, made a permanent fort and renamed Fort Stewart, has succeeded in dodging all the military cuts, even the last big base closures that Congress passed.

Fort Stewart still provides a good way of making a living for the people around Gum Branch and occasionally something to talk about, like the night a big black bear wandered into town from the swamps and was struck by a car. The injured bear climbed a tree right across from the courthouse for safety. The sheriff called animal control at Fort Stewart for assistance. They came out and shot the bear with a tranquilizer gun, but unfortunately the dart struck his heart and the bear died.

Meanwhile, the sheriff's department got a report of a car fire about five miles down the road in Allenhurst. When they got there, they found this drunk GI sitting on the side of the road next to his burning car, crying. When questioned, he said that he had hit this old man wearing a fur coat in Hinesville and had intended to burn his car and report it stolen so he wouldn't get caught for being a hit-and-run driver. But after he thought about the old man running off, hollering like a bear, he just couldn't live with it and decided to give himself up. The bear was taken to a taxidermist and now stands guard at the county jail, sporting a badge and a deputy's hat.

TALMADGE

For almost two weeks there had been a fine mist dropping like it usually does in the fall in southeast Georgia. I had been trying to finish a front porch on our little place and get back to my family in Tampa, but the drizzle had hampered my progress.

"Russell, what in the world are you doing out here working in the rain?" Talmadge appeared as if from nowhere.

"It ain't raining, this is just a Georgia dew," I told him.

"Why don't you go in there and put on some dry clothes and ride over to Jesup with me?" he asked.

I thought about it for a second and let my natural instincts for procrastination take over.

167

"It won't take me but a few minutes."

The roads were muddy from the weeks of foul weather, and the truck slipped and slid occasionally. Talmadge would automatically steer with the slide as I had watched him do over the last forty years or so, maintaining perfect control. My mind drifted back through the years and I remembered that after I moved to Florida I went to a lot of race tracks to watch the professional drivers, and I realized that my cousin Talmadge was as good as any of them.

Then there was the time when I was fourteen and rode my old army surplus Harley to Gum Branch. I know he had never even touched a motorcycle before. All I had to do was to show him where the controls were, and the next thing I knew he was headed to Ludowici down eleven miles of the worst dirt roads in the country to see his girlfriend Judy.

If he ever fell, he didn't tell anybody about it. When he was in high school and eighteen years old, he applied for a chauffeur's license and got the job of driving the school bus until he graduated. I remember watching him maneuver an old Minneapolis Moline tractor pulling logs out of the swamp with the front wheels up in the air. His touch was so perfect that the tractor kept pulling and the front tires never touched down until the log came up on dry ground.

The only time that I know he ever had an accident was when he and I drove his brother Miles' old cut-down Ford to Ludowici. We had just cruised the block-long main street beside the railroad tracks and were turning around when he nicked the bumper of a Studebaker parked nose-end to the curb. The only thing that hit were the two hubcaps on my side, and they popped off and went rattling out in the street. A highway patrolman came over while we were picking up the hubcaps and wrote Talmadge a ticket. I thought it was for reckless driving; Talmadge remembered it as careless driving. The only thing he pled guilty to was disturbing the peace.

"Why we going to Jesup?" I asked, not that I needed an excuse to leave my work.

"To see somebody in the hospital," he answered.

"Somebody sick?"

"Yep, the hospital is always full of sick people," he said.

"No, you know what I mean ... is there anybody we know in the hospital?" I said.

"I don't think so," he said.

I dropped it at that and we started talking about things in general. It amazed me that Talmadge always knew how I felt about things like integrity and our unspoken obligation to God, and he openly recognized the difference between church doctrine and the Bible.

Talmadge had a built-in guide about "right and wrong" that he followed. He understood that I had the same, but I had trouble following mine.

We talked about all the Army trucks full of solders that had run off the road and sunk into the muddy waters as we crossed the Altamaha Swamp, and the stink of the plastics plant on the banks of the river.

The little hospital in Jesup had a bad reputation back in the '40s. People said you might remember going in but you wouldn't remember coming out. We walked in the door. "Hello, Mr. Groover, how are you doing today?" greeted the receptionist

"Just fine, Shirley. My goodness, you get prettier ever time I see you," Talmadge said. "I want you to meet my cousin from Tampa."

Shirley nodded, acknowledging my presence, then said, "Mr. Groover, you'll tell a girl anything. Just go right on in."

We walked down the hall filled with hospital sounds and smells. Every so often, Talmadge would look in an open door and greet the patient; they would respond with a greeting of their own and call him "Talmadge" or "Mr. Groover." At the end of the hall we looked in a room and saw an old man lying motionless, staring at the ceiling.

"How you doing today?" Talmadge said.

The old man looked over with half-glazed eyes, then turned away without answering. Talmadge walked on into the room with a purpose and pulled up a chair and sat down.

"What they got you in here for? You don't look

like you're sick to me," Talmadge said.

"I'm in here to die," the old man responded in an aggravated tone.

Talmadge ignored the man's attitude and said, "I'm from over at Gum Branch on the other side of Ludowici ... do you know where that is?"

"Yeah, I know where that is. I used to work at Camp Stewart during the war," he said.

"You don't look that old to me," Talmadge said.

"I'm eighty-three years old," he said.

"My name is Talmadge Groover. What's yours?"

"George Anderson," the old man responded.

For thirty minutes I watched as Talmadge talked to George about everything from the war to farming, and I saw the spark of life come back into George's eyes when Talmadge disagreed with his opinion of President Reagan. The conversation was brought to an end by the nurse telling us that Mister Anderson would have to eat his lunch now. Talmadge got up and shook George's hand and told him he would see him next week when he stopped back by. As we walked down the hall the nurse caught up with us and said, "Mr. Groover we thank you so much. Mr. Anderson hadn't responded to anyone in a week. I think he had lost the will to live."

"Debby, you take care of yourself now. We'll see you later," Talmadge said to the nurse.

Back in the truck, I asked Talmadge how he knew that old man was in the hospital and needed someone to talk to? All he said was, "There are people everywhere that need help; you don't have to look far to find them. Besides, I'm a deacon and that's my job. How about we stop at Captain Joe's and eat some shrimp?"

As we left downtown Jesup I thought of all the people that I had heard criticize Talmadge over the last few years since he had his first heart attack; they talked about him not doing anything with his time. I hope any one of them will accomplish as much in their life as I had just seen him accomplish.

Talmadge had diabetes in 1993 to the point that he had circulation problems in his legs and the doctors were talking amputation. At that time, on one of my trips back to Florida from North Carolina I had made it a point to stop by just to visit with him. The October air had been a little chilly as we talked about the things that our fathers and our grandpa had probably talked about, the Bible, politics, and the last war. He had been in good spirits when I left, and he told me to bring our cousin Lawrence back with me the next time I came. Now, as we talked in the pickup, I determined to remember to do that.

That next December I returned with Lawrence to Gum Branch, but it was to attend Talmadge's funeral. He had had a heart attack and died instantly right after he and his wife Judy finished putting up Christmas lights. It was swift and almost painless. God had spared him the pain and helpless feeling of being an amputee.

After the funeral I cried, not for Talmadge but for myself, his grandchildren, his family, and for all the people who will miss him. Lawrence and I openly criticized the ministers who conducted his funeral because they didn't even come close to paying Talmadge homage. Now as I write this, I find myself, who knew and loved him so well, not able to do him justice, either.

I guess the best I can say is: Talmadge, this book is for you.

Area where the story takes place in Georgia.

174

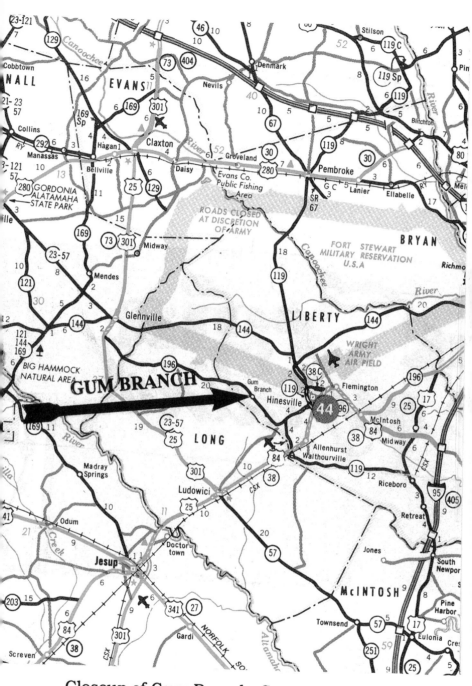

Closeup of Gum Branch, Georgia location.

175

Sin
5/20/2003
PGB

not that good.